Rambling Rosie Runyon

John & July,

This tale would not have been gosilk without you!

John L. Stump

JOHN L. STUMP

Copyright @ 2021 by John L. Stump

ISBN: 978-1-954693-10-4

FV-14
Manufactured in the United States of America

First Edition 2021

Author contact: Doc@DocStump.com www.DocStump.com

Published by:
www.IntellectPublishing.com

Preface

She was a heroine of Allegheny and Appalachian Mountain lore: a midwife, a sharpshooter, medicine woman and gold miner. This woman was real. The author tells of his grandmother's exploits throughout the United States from 1886 to 1978. We follow her most interesting life from the east coast of Virginia to the west coast of the Yukon Territory.

From President McKinley to Jimmy Carter, she was a staunch political supporter of freedom and women's rights. She survived the Spanish flu, World War I, and still managed a family of four children and three marriages. Her rambling and skills will amaze readers.

JOHN L. STUMP

Dedication

To the grandchildren and great-grandchildren of Rosie Runyon Smith Pendergrass, plus the many friends and relatives that were called on along her life journey.

JOHN L. STUMP

Acknowledgments

Many thanks to those who helped make this book possible: Dianne Stump, Ron Johnson, Len Breitfeller, and Judy Richards. And a heartfelt thanks to Carol Anne Smith, the daughter of William H. Smith, and granddaughter of Rosie Runyon Smith, who worked tirelessly on correcting much of the family inaccuracies compiled over the years.

Thank you, Carol Anne.

JOHN L. STUMP

Foreword

Everyone has heard of Annie Oakley, Calamity Jane, Pocahontas and Nellie Bly; these legendary figures started life as pioneer girls. Well, Rambling Rosie Runyon was equivalent to all those, and she was real. In the eyes of her grandson, she was larger than life. Dr. John Stump tells of the adventures he was told as a young man sitting at the feet of his grandmother in the hollows of West Virginia. He revisited these stories as the family moved from South Carolina, Florida and the Delmarva Peninsula when she was in her 90s.

It has taken him fifty years to finally get these tales down on paper. Now you, the reader, can sort out fact from fiction of the exciting life and times of Rambling Rosie Runyon.

JOHN L. STUMP

*Rosie Runyon and her daughter Nora
Mae, Welch, West Virginia 1958*

Rambling Rosie Runyon

JOHN L. STUMP

Chapter 1

No matter where I roam, Virginia will always be home!

Derby Daze

This story is based on the life of my grandmother. She lived to be 95 years of age when many people thought she wouldn't make it through her adolescent years. She was my mother's mother, daughter of John Henry Runyon and Sylvia S. Deel of Virginia.

Grandma Rosie, as I called her for a long time, described her home in the Virginia countryside much like someone describes the French countryside: the green hills, the little stone churches, the sloping pastures filled with sleepy-eyed cows. She told me she loved the outdoor life her family farm afforded her on their fifty acres of timber and farmland.

Her memory was still acute as she was telling me the story of her early childhood.

"My father worked hard to forge out a living by working as a farmer and horse trainer for a wealthy land baron of Kentucky. Mr. Claiborne had offices in Washington, D.C. and New York, and used Kentucky to relax. He was what was called an industrialist during those days, with over a thousand acres to care for in

Virginia and Kentucky," Grandma Rosie said, as we sat by the old coal-fired cook stove late one winter evening in February. We were drinking sassafras tea together as she talked.

"We lived in an area where Virginia, Kentucky and West Virginia were just a stone's throw away from each other. I think we lived in Kentucky then. Dad worked in Virginia on this big farm some folks like us called an estate. Maybe it was the other way around; I can't rightly remember because we moved twice when I was very young. Back and forth between Kentucky, Virginia and then West Virginia back to Kentucky. Each time we moved it seemed like only a few miles, but I think it was because our family was growing, and I didn't realize it.

"My father's responsibility, besides our farm, was to manage the fifty horses the Claiborne family owned. The Claiborne family had been involved with horses since the Civil War. The family enterprise traces back to Virginia, and at some point, after the Civil War, it moved to Kentucky.

"Claiborne thought he had a shot at the Kentucky Derby the year I began to pay attention to adult things. He had a prime interest in Ben Ali, a horse owned by his colleague James Ben Ali, from Turkey. The number one jockey, Duffy, was going to ride him, I heard them say.

"A lot of history and pride was heaped on this farm, especially the horses. This meant the duties of my father, John Henry Runyon, were the care for the horses' every need from six in the morning until six in the evening. It was well known everyone called him 'Henry the Horseman' on the farm in those days. He knew everything about each horse as if they were his children, like me: age, name, hands, weight, unusual tendencies and so forth. If anything happened to one of the horses, he always felt it was his responsibility to take care of the injury; rarely was there a need for a veterinary call in those days. You might say Dad was a vet without the certification or schooling."

"Who was his number-one jockey that year, Grandma Rosie?" I asked her.

"I was only a little tyke then, but I do remember my father being very protective of the horse called Ben Ali the year I started going with him to the farm. There were several jockeys around because I asked Dad who those men were that were only as tall as me. That year Dad said Paul Duffy needed to ride the ride of his career. I was really too young to understand the significance of what that meant at the time, but later realized Mr. Claiborne stood to make a huge amount of money at the Derby.

"The talk I heard around the farm was Mr. Claiborne really knew these horses, and what he didn't know my father did. I was very gratified to be able to go watch the horses run as they were being trained."

Rosie Rides

"My older sister Sarah and I both loved horses. We had been around horses since we could walk and climb on their back. We had only three at home to care for since Mom didn't ride anymore for some reason unknown to me. The responsibility fell on Sarah and me since Dad had bought us a horse when Sarah turned ten.

"Earlier that year I had gotten my horse. The year before, Sarah received hers. I learned from Sarah what and how to do everything in the care of the horses around eight or nine. It wasn't as easy as our dog Shep." She describes a dog much like Lassie of early TV fame. "Sarah was very patient and motherly toward me then.

"Father had secured both horses from the Claiborne herd he had to care for. Something was unusual about them but at that time I didn't know, and really didn't care—I was so thrilled to get a horse. He could have been missing a tail and I would have never known until later.

"Dad said they were both two years old, which was significant for some reason. Sarah's was white and mine

Mom rides Diablo

black. The boys all had horses while they were living home but now only Sarah and I were living with our parents, so the responsibility fell to us."

"It seemed that some of the racehorses were to be put out to pasture when they got something wrong or they were too old. That was where our horses came from, I heard Dad tell someone.

"Sarah told me one day, 'Rosie, you and I are now in training to be horse trainers under Dad, or horse nurses,' as he called us. Because Dad brings a horse to our farm from time to time, we have to massage, slowly walk, and put liniment on their legs each day, things that require more individual time. But I loved the personal time with the horses, it helped me as much as it did them, I believe.

"I laughed at the new title I now had. I told Sarah and all my school friends, I had just finished the sixth grade and was a horse nurse! For the next year sister and I rode all over the place. The only thing Dad had said was, 'Be sure you stay on our property when you ride each day.'

"We stayed on the property when we rode; the property some of which Dad had never seen, especially the mountainous thicket of rocks and unusable forest on the northwest section of the farm. One day we rode up in that section where there was heavy, low, shrub growth and a lot of saplings of maple, oak, cedar, pine and other trees that had sprouted up with the spring rains.

"Sarah's horse, White Cloud, reared-up and made strange noises through his nose. Sarah yelled, 'Look out, Rosie, there's a big snake to your left, about ten feet away on that hillside.' My horse, Diablo, had already seen the snake and was pulling away to the opposite side. Diablo reared and almost threw me off, but I held tight to the reins until Diablo was out of striking distance of the snake. Then I said, 'Sarah, we better ask Dad if we can carry a sidearm or a .30-30 to protect ourselves out here.'"

"Sarah replied, 'Rosie, I agree. Let's see if Dad or Uncle Bill will teach us to shoot. It's something that we both may need at some point if we keep riding in these areas. We could even add hunting small game to bring home for dinner, which would help out at home. We'll ask Mom to teach us how to clean, process and cook them for eating in order not to be more work for her at home.'

"'It's a deal, we'll ask Dad tonight at dinner.'"

"We've always had a family-style dinner in the evening. To Dad and Mom, it meant all of us could sit at the table and discuss our day's events in harmony and peace. It was normal to start with Mom, Dad, Sarah then me because I was the youngest. I told him what happened to Sarah and me on the trail that day. How the rattlesnake had nearly struck Diablo and me. When I thought about Diablo dying or being hurt by the snake it made me almost break down into tears and it seemed to pull on Dad's heart strings."

Rosie's first poem

Rosie Runyon, my name is saucy! Rosie has five letters,
oh how classy.
It begins with R ends with R,
and that's bizarre!

8

Just like Diablo in the end,
my horse is more than just my friend!

Rosie and Sarah Learn to Shoot

"Father was reluctant but agreed when we told him about the snake almost being close enough to strike Sarah and me. The next day father took us to the Claiborne ranch where we were introduced to many of the hired hands, and one in particular by the name of Jake Mullins. Jake took us to a shooting range the men had made there on the ranch where they practiced each week to keep their skills up, the man told us.

"'Most of the men here on the ranch shoot but are not what you would call good with a gun,'" Jake added.

"Jake asked us both to go separately into a special box-like area, where we were told to wait until he returned. 'I am going to set up the targets for each of you,' he told us. Jake was a grown man of around thirty or maybe forty, I'm not sure; but I do remember he had a distinct limp, as if one leg was longer or shorter than the other. He was a nice-looking man with blond hair, blue eyes and fair skin, a bit scruffy but probably looked good cleaned up on Saturday night." And she grinned as she talked about Jake.

"When Jake returned, he showed each of us his Colt .45 six-shooter he called a sidearm. It had a long silver barrel with a white ivory handle. He emptied the cylinder of bullets and counted out six. Then he spun the cylinder and asked each of us to hold the gun, put it to our side and then lift it up several times. The gun seemed heavy to me,

9

so I asked Jake, 'Can I use two hands? The gun seems heavy after lifting it several times. I'm only twelve. I know Sarah is older and bigger, but I really want to learn so just give me a chance.'"

"'Don't worry," Jake said, 'this will come as second nature in a few months. Now, the next stage is to learn to load and unload your sidearm safely and quickly. You will each take all the shells out and count each one as you take them out, don't let anything distract you. Then reload the same way, count and recount each time. Do this each day five times before you think about firing.

"'The final stage is after you have the sidearm loaded, lift the gun and very carefully aim at the target. This is a little different for everyone. Look at the end of the barrel and you will see a little piece of metal sticking up; that is what is called a sight. I am left-handed, completely opposite from most people, so I had to learn how to shoot right-handed first, and later learn left-handed. That's how I became famous in shooting circles; I can shoot with either hand or both at the same time. Now, Sarah, let's you start first.'

"We went on to spend the morning practicing all that Jake had taught us. He told us we were to meet him there each Monday, Wednesday and Friday morning at 8:30 a.m. to practice all of the skills with the sidearm. This went on a month because it was May, school was out, and we had time to devote to shooting and riding. I was beginning to feel at ease with the sidearm.

"Then, one morning in July, Jake brought a rifle to class

with him. It was a .30-30 Winchester. I was familiar with the .30-30 since that was what Dad had hanging up over the door at home.

"Jake said, 'You may be out riding and decide to hunt for rabbit, squirrel, or some morning just see a deer. I know you girls don't like to shoot them because they are pretty and cute but that's how many people eat by shooting small game, and the deer is still considered small game. We don't use our sidearm if an animal is over fifty or sixty feet away. Your shot becomes more inaccurate past fifty or sixty feet. You then pull your rifle. The .30-30 is my go-to weapon when I'm riding or even walking in the hills for that matter. Today we are going to begin the next phase of your gun education. We will go through the same procedure we did with the sidearm. You will notice the shells get progressively larger as the gun changes caliber.'

"We went through the .30-30 each day after the sidearm practice that now took only half the time it did in the beginning. Jake explained caliber and why it changes.

"The rifle was considerably more difficult for me because of my small stature and age but I never let that hinder my trying. It took several weeks before I could even hold the gun to aim the .30-30 accurately.

"I remember the first day, about two or three weeks later, I was able to hold the .30-30 up, aim and fire at the target, Jake and Sarah were shocked. 'Look, look Rosie, you hit the target. Not a bull's eye but you hit the target; that's better than most men can do,' Jake said, with a big broad smile.

"That is how Sarah and I became crack shots early in life. I went back home and spent another two or three hours shooting in the afternoon or evening. By the end of that year, I could shoot as well if not better than most men on the Claiborne ranch. I never joined any contest or showed off my skill because my father said that was not the purpose of learning the weapons."

Chapter 2

Grandma Rosie's Golden Rules.
1. *Don't go where you are not invited.*
2. *Don't talk about what you don't know.*
3. *Don't interfere with things that are none of your business.*

Grandma Rosie

As far back as I can remember Grandma Rosie was in my life. The very first memory to stay in my mind was our family living in Bluewell, the name of the farm Dad and Mom bought outside of Bluefield, Virginia. I think my dad was working at a mine in Grundy, Virginia, or Gary, West Virginia; that location was convenient for him getting to work.

I was then three, nearly four. We had a small farm with chickens, cows, hogs, and horses. Grandma Rosie would take me out picking blackberries, strawberries and different greens. The one memory most vivid in my mind was the day she lifted me up on her horse for my first ride in the saddle. She showed me where to hold and she walked around the farm what seemed like nearly a mile with me in the saddle. Then we would go collect eggs and feed the animals. Evidently, we didn't have running water because Granny and I would bring in two or three buckets of water from a big round stone well in our back yard. There was a bucket tied on to a rope and a person, usually

Grandma Rosie, would crank it down to the water and fill the pail, crank it back up full, then take it in the house to pour into a larger tub or bucket that was kept in the kitchen close to the sink to use. I remember this because I asked if I could help and when I tried, I spilled the entire bucket of water all over me. Granny had to take me into the house to change clothes.

Mom must have worked during this time because Grandma Rosie would make me breakfast and lunch each day. I knew one thing for sure—it was a lot of fun when Grandma was doing it with me, no matter what it was we were doing.

Only One Cook in the Kitchen

Another memory I have of Grandma Rosie was when I was about five or six. We were living in South Carolina then and Grandma Rosie had come to our house down there a week or two before. I was getting ready for school and Mom usually prepared breakfast since I was expected to eat before going to school. It surprised me when Mom had not made breakfast, but Granny had instead prepared my favorite, hot biscuits with hot apples and strawberry jam. For some reason this always seemed like a treat rather than just breakfast.

"Granny, where is Mom? This is not my usual eggs, bacon and gravy. When did you learn to cook?"

She glanced up from the old wood cook stove and said, "Johnny, I've been cooking a long time. I'm not quite certain when I was called a cook, but my mother used to say, 'There's only room for one cook in the kitchen at a time.'

"I must have been around ten or eleven. Sarah had already started to cook breakfast for everyone. She would always be expected in the kitchen an hour earlier than the rest of the family. Dad got up at five and expected breakfast to be ready after he and Sarah got dressed and washed up. They both went to work earlier than the rest of the family.

"Mom and I would get up around six. I think it was because we had such a small family, our kitchen table would only seat four. Dad had always said, 'Workers have to wash up, eat first, then the kids,' until Sarah took over breakfast chores.

"We didn't have running water in the house or a bathroom in those days. The water was from the well first and after that Dad installed a big blue iron pump with a fancy wooden handle on the back porch. Our toilet, then called an 'Out House' was on the other side of the main house, about fifty feet away. Everyone had to pump their own water when they were old enough and bring it in the house to wash up. Most men just washed their face and hands before breakfast, then went to work.

"Mother and we children ate the second shift; at one time there were just the four of us. Sarah and I hardly knew my older brothers, Jake and Bob. They were more than ten years older than I was.

"We were early birds, got up early, came in late, and

got married before I was old enough to know what was going on. A year after Sarah started cooking it was then my turn to serve breakfast, and then Sarah prepared lunch. The meal called supper, many call dinner, took much longer to learn, and Momma always prepared dinner. Back then we ate deer, rabbit, squirrel and even coon as a main course when in the dead of winter and meat was scarce. Times were hard but we survived because we worked together as a family."

"Granny, you'll have to tell me about dinner another time. It's time for the school bus and I better not miss it, or I will get a licking from Dad when he gets home from the coal mines."

"You're right, Johnny, get going, and don't linger anywhere after school, your mom has a new job and she has to leave earlier, and comes home late because she has to ride with Mrs. Pruitt down the street."

We were still living in South Carolina. The doctors had told my adoptive father, John Fleming Stump, after he was injured in a huge slate fall that killed many in Gary, West Virginia in 1951, to forget coal mining with his injuries, go south, retire in the sunshine. However, if they had known my father, he was not about to retire.

He found that U.S. Steel Corporation and DuPont Corporation were hiring structural builders to build the New Ellenton Energy Plant in New Ellenton, a town just a few miles southeast of Augusta, Georgia. Our family moved from Welch, West Virginia to Aiken, South Carolina for that job. I was nearly five then and that's how we ended up living in Aiken, a few miles from Augusta and New Ellenton.

Our home in Aiken was on a sandy road. The dirt was not like in West Virginia. There, the soil was dark, almost black, and many times you couldn't tell the dirt from the coal dust that had fallen to the ground from coal trains and trucks. In Aiken the soil was sandy and light like what you would find at the beach. The plants were different than what I had learned from Grandma Rosie in West Virginia. Were we now going to have to start over learning the trees, plants and herbs here as well, I thought?

Grandma Rosie came to live with us again after we had moved. She came to live with us that year because my father and mother had to work, there were few if any people that would care for outside children if they were not family at that time in the rural South. I found that many of our neighbors were doing the same thing, asking "Grandmother" to care for the next generation.

Grandma Rosie was what I was asked to call her by my father. However, later that year Grandma Rosie and I were sitting in a swing my dad had made in the back yard. I said, "Grandma Rosie, do you want me to push you higher in the swing? It's fun."

"No, Johnny, I don't need to go high when I swing, now that I'm old. That's for when you are young; you are more daring than old folks."

"You mean like you now, Grandma Rosie?"

"Yes, but each time we talk you don't have to continue

to use 'Grandma Rosie'. I know you are addressing me. Just say, 'Granny'."

She smiled. When she did, her gold tooth showed. I smiled and said, "Granny, I can see your gold tooth when you smile really big like that."

"Yes, that means I am happy and all those around are in good fortune. That gold was brought back from the Klondike where me and your grandfather went when we were young." She smiled again.

"Why did you put it in your mouth?" I asked her.

"Well, back in those days, in that era, you had to keep what you had of value close, and what's closer than your mouth? It's hidden but in plain sight for all to see."

"Granny, that's pretty good and not many people would think of that."

"I have to give credit to Chief Montokau for the stimulation of my brain to think like that. When my sister Sarah and I were young we were allowed to go study with the Indians. The Chief always carried a small bag tied around his neck. I asked one of our teachers what was in the little bag? One elder medicine man said it was his most prized possession.

"When my husband Tom gave the gold to me, I thought I would put it around my neck. But Tom had a better idea. We would put it in our mouth!" And she smiled again, real big.

I knew then we were buddies. Granny stayed with us that year until school started in the fall. Mom's schedule changed so that she could be home when I got back. A week after school started, Granny got on a Greyhound bus and went somewhere, much to my regret.

The next time Granny came to live with us, I was going into the third grade. She had come from Virginia or West Virginia where she was living with one of her other children, my cousin's mom said. Mom also said, "Your dad has been transferred to another job site. We'll be moving because it's too far for your dad to drive each day."

We then moved to a place called Little River near Myrtle Beach, South Carolina.

I never knew what was so secret about that place, but Mom said we would only be there a short time to do a special job for DuPont; that was all I was ever told.

That summer was great. Granny and I went on long hikes down these old roads piled high in sand; she would use her cane to point out different plants and their names as well as their use. The wildflowers growing alongside of the road Granny knew most of the names for, but there were many she said were new to her. There were no cars that passed; it was like a desolate area. It looked like the river had washed the sand up on the roads. The trees were huge, with moss hanging down from their limbs. Granny said, "They are Live Oaks." That seemed silly to me; of course, they were live.

One day we walked further in a different direction than usual and we came up to a river. It was black, smooth and cool to the touch. Under the shade of one of those big trees, we sat down on a log for a rest. Granny set her cane down and was cutting a piece of apple for us to eat. I asked Granny if I could jump in and take a swim. She was reluctant but I, of course, was persistent and stripped down to my skivvies, then jumped in headfirst. The cool black water felt good on that hot July afternoon.

All of a sudden, I heard Granny yelling, screaming like I'd never heard from her. She was flailing her arms and motioning for me to come in her direction. I started swimming toward her when I noticed out of the corner of my eye motion in the water near me. I swam faster and harder for the shore and just as I reached the shore and started climbing out of the water a big gator opened its mouth no more than three feet away.

Granny said, "Get up there and get your clothes. I'll try to distract his attention."

I ran over to the log and looked back at Granny. She was pounding and thumping the gator's head. I grabbed my clothes and shouted for Granny. She screeched and bellowed while slamming her shillelagh down on its head. Right then, for a second or two, I felt sorry for the gator. We got out of there and never went back to that area on our walks again.

Often, I would overhear Granny telling Mom a story about when she was young like the following story.

Riding the rails

Granny said, "I had been married to Tom Smith, a young engineer on the Norfolk-Western Railway out of Norfolk, Virginia, since I was about seventeen. But the way we met was quite unconventional when I think back on it.

"I was a young teenager, no more than thirteen or fourteen. I hitched rides on the trains that came through the town where we lived in Virginia and Kentucky, much like many other children, mostly boys. But every now and then you would find a girl or two hanging out on the back of a freight train. We were not hobos but just liked the excitement of the steam engine and the freight trains.

"Sarah and I started doing it together. I won't say she got me into it, but I followed her in about everything. One day, nearly a month or two after we had been hopping on the trains, there was one with an empty boxcar. Sarah's foot slipped while hopping on. She was wearing a long blue gingham dress with a petticoat and the dress and petticoat got tangled in the rigging of the train, which tore her dress and petticoat nearly clean off before I could pull her into the boxcar. She was crying, cussing, and questioning what she was going to do with the rags she was left with as a dress. I wore overalls almost all the time, except when I had to go to church, to town, or something like that with Mom and Dad.

"Anyway, we took some of the petticoat, tore it into pieces in order to cover her behind and other parts until we could get her home through the woods. We never told Mom or Dad about the incident until many years later

21

when Sarah was getting ready to get married. After that harrowing ride, Sarah was reluctant to go with me many times.

"However, I didn't stop. I loved riding the trains, going new places, seeing new things. I just couldn't seem to get enough. "

Young Love

Granny continued, "I liked going to new places and destinations. Mom and Dad thought I was out riding my horse, but I often left Diablo with a school friend and would hop or hobo a train and go wherever it went for the day. I would usually ride in an empty boxcar going to Lexington, Louisville, somewhere I knew was close, and I could catch another return train in an hour or two.

"After doing this five or six times, I thought I knew the system well enough, until one day the train changed tracks without me realizing what was happening. The train took me to Bristol, Virginia. Before I could figure out what to do, a railroad inspector caught me outside of the boxcar, thought I was a boy stealing, and took me to the engineer of the train, a tall, handsome young man by the name of Tom Smith."

"'What were you doing on this train, Missy?' the engineer asked.

"I said to him, 'I love to ride trains, to see new places I haven't been. It just makes me feel free and unrestricted. It allows me time to think. I'm able to relax, especially when the sun is shining and I'm going somewhere new.'

"'You had no intentions of theft or robbery?' The young engineer looked at her as he spoke in a pointed manner.

"'Are you kidding? I'm only fifteen. My dad would shoot you and me if he thought I was anywhere around a train. I'm supposed to be practicing my riding skills, but my sister and I heard two hobos talking about how nice it was riding the train for free.'

"'I'll tell you what, I won't turn you in if you promise to let me know when you get a hankering to ride the train again. I come by the Bristol, Grundy and Bluefield stops every Monday, Wednesday and Friday, going east. Every Tuesday, and Thursday and Saturday going west. I'm off on Sunday after I go to church. Do you go to church young lady?'

"'Why, yes, yes, I do, as a matter of fact,' I told him.

"'Well, this Sunday ask the Lord to forgive you for the trespassing you and your sister have done over the past month or two with the Norfolk-Western Railway. I'll take you back to where you got on the train this time but if it happens again, I'm going to have to talk to your father; or Mr. Evans here will have to visit your family and ask why they are not keeping better control of their two girls.'

"I noticed a smile at the corners of his mouth when he was talking. It looked like he was trying to hold back from smiling or laughing. But I pretended not to notice because Mr. Evans, the inspector, was there with us, and he was an old man of 40 or 50 anyway, my father's age.

23

"'Yes, sir. I'll follow every detailed instruction you have advised.' I made sure they both understood I would not hobo the train again, and my sister nor I ever did again. But the following Tuesday I was out there by the tracks, and when Tom went by, he slowed the train down, waved and blew the whistle. I did this on a regular time schedule for a week.

"Then the next week he stopped the train and let me sit in the engineer's seat while he stood beside me. This went on for several weeks. One day the fireman went to the caboose to get something. Tom was talking, describing something about his engine; he looked so handsome, I just leaned up and kissed him. That was the beginning of our courtship.

"Tom at first treated me like a little sister as I rode with him and his fireman on the train all over the southeast. One day we were coming from a town near Louisville called "Whiskers," named after Joseph Beard, a man of means who donated land to the railroad for a station. I noticed Tom's attitude toward me changed after that day. He seemed like he wanted to see me all the time, every day.

"Tom was well educated from the University of Kentucky in Lexington, before going to the University of Virginia to become a railroad engineer. Tom said, 'Rosie, you have the essentials that every woman wishes they had. You can cook, sew, plus you have beauty, in addition you can hunt, shoot, ride and you are a medicine woman. Even though you haven't yet finished the seventh grade, you are a full woman.'

"He sure didn't hold being older and more educated

over me. He added, 'You have a skill set no one can get in college. In addition, it's a more practical better education for what you want and need.'

"After nearly a year of dilly-dallying and flirting with each other, I invited him home and introduced him to Mom and Dad. It wasn't long before Tom Smith asked for my hand in marriage. I was going to be seventeen, he was twenty-six.

"We were young, in love and wanted some adventure in our life together before we started a family. Tom told me that he really liked reading Mark Twain and Huck Finn's tales when he was in college but had never gotten to go anywhere. Tom said he was ready to take Teddy Roosevelt at his word, that Life is a great adventure."

Chapter 3

*Away up high in the tree, two red apples wait for me.
I shook that tree hard as could be, and down came the apples,
yummy were they good!*

-Rosie Runyon 1903

Gold in Them Thar Hills

One day, soon after the marriage, we took a short aunt for a railroad meeting Tom had in Columbus, Ohio. While there, we saw a newspaper stating there was a big new gold find in the Yukon Territory. People were leaving their homes, jobs and family to go there to get rich fast. I asked Tom where the Yukon Territory was, and if he thought the strike was for real.

"He said, 'I don't know, Rosie, but we could go there and see. Sometimes these sensational headlines are just that, all print and no meat. If there's a railroad up there, I can get us a ride, and maybe even get me a job while you look for gold.' And he laughed very hard, as if never believing I could find gold.

"Sure enough, a few days later Tom said, 'Rosie, we're on our way to the Yukon gold rush. I have us a ride almost all the way. Our railroad, the Norfolk-Western, has agreements with the other railway lines that have passenger trains, or are soon to be completed, with agreements. The boss wasn't sure about a job in the West or Canada because his authority only extends to the eastern half of the United States. But he thinks once they find that I'm an engineer I won't have any problem with employment. That's a pretty good blessing from one of the top engineers in Virginia,' Tom said.

"We left that week for parts unknown. Mom and Dad were sad to see me leave but they were pleased that we were happy. Dad only said, 'Rosie, love is blind, but marriage needs a great deal of patience and work. It should be a 50/50 relationship.' He kissed me on the cheek, something he rarely did, and a big tear came to his eye as he turned and left.

"Later, I thought about the emotional aspect. I was his baby daughter leaving home. Sarah had just gotten married the year before. Mom and Dad would be all alone.

"As we were getting on the train, Tom was helping with my bag and said, 'Rosie, what's this long, hard thing in your carpetbag?' I carried a carpetbag my mother had given me after Tom told her we were going on a long trip. I had packed this beautiful new carpetbag that was a part of my wedding gift. I laughed, and said, 'Why, Tom, it's my gun. A proper young lady doesn't travel anywhere without her cannon. Let me introduce you to Nell, my trusty Colt .45. Jake, my shooting teacher, gave this to me as a gift a few years ago. If I could have found a way, I would have brought Diablo and my .30-30, as well.' Tom just shook his head, grinned and said, 'I should have known, a girl doesn't leave home without her essentials.'

"It took two days by train to get back to Ohio. We got off in the busy little city of Cincinnati for a few days to look around. Tom found that the N&W didn't go any further but had an agreement with Union Pacific to carry passengers west to St. Louis, Missouri, where another change was necessary. We stayed in St. Louis for two days, then caught another train with the Union Pacific Express to Seattle, Washington, a week train trip further. However, this is where we had a real problem.

"When we got to Wyoming, all of a sudden the train stopped. The conductor came to each passenger car and told everyone the railway temporarily had to stop here. There would be a 2- to 4-week delay on the track being laid, due to some type of unforeseen damage. We could either stay in Cheyenne at railroad expense or continue on by horse and wagon in a caravan.

"Tom and I spent two days in the town of Cheyenne, a lovely little town, full of cowboys, wild horses, herds of cattle and fighting Indians. The old wooden hotel with ten full rooms kept the bar and diner busy. But it soon got boring; we decided to head west with a wagon train formed by the rail company. We were going to take the horse and wagon provided by the rail company.

"'Rosie, this is dangerous territory they told me in the hotel saloon, if we choose to take the wagon with the wagon train of 15 to 20 covered wagons, which is the same as the Wells Fargo Trail. We must stay on the main trail, and even then, there are desperados, bands of drunks, and

Indians roaming the prairie from time to time that want to take your money and aren't afraid to attack a small wagon train and take your life in the process.'

"I reminded Tom that Chief Matuka of the Cherokee Indian Tribe, once part of the Shattars Tribe, took Grandmother Elizabeth Finley hostage. I never could keep those names straight, but I have Indian blood from that affair. I was even able to study with the Indian medicine man when I was only twelve through some type of an agreement with the Indian Authority. 'I wonder if that will help us out here now?' I asked Tom.

"Tom laughed and said, 'I hope something helps. I'm not one for shooting and killing but I think I'm going to buy me a rifle before we make this journey on toward our west coast destination.'

"'Tom, take my advice, get a little Winchester .30-30.' That's what I had, and my father had one as well, a great little rifle. They are light, easy to handle and accurate to shoot up to 150 yards or maybe 200 if you are really good.' Tom took my advice and bought a previously owned Winchester in the local gun shop and put it in the wagon under the seat he sat in most of the time. Tom usually drove the horses because he said I could shoot quickly from a seated position. He had to stand to shoot, like a hunter. As a result, I usually took the shotgun seat.

"We spent a week in that covered wagon and didn't see a person going or coming except in our wagon train. That area was beautiful to look at but was what my father used to call, 'God forsaken.' The next town we came to after Cheyenne was Laramie and it also was over-run with the same thing—ranchers, cowboys, and Indians, drinking and fighting.

"We loaded up at the general store with the other travelers. We asked about a hotel and the store keep looked at me like I had lost my mind. He said, 'Lady, if you and your husband want a decent place to sleep and bath, keep going to the next town called Rollins. It has a nice family-type hotel, but here it's full of cheap women and cowboys.'

Rosie's westward wagon train

"We kept going toward Rollins where we unfortunately split off from the wagon train a little too early. We encountered a couple of desperados looking for trouble just about a mile out of Rollins.

"Two men, each riding a horse with saddlebags and rifle sling, stopped our wagon, pretending they were lost and needed help. I still was riding shotgun and Tom was driving the wagon. That day Tom had pulled a blanket up over my legs because there was a cool wind in the morning. When they approached, I eased my pistol into my right hand; for some reason I really didn't trust these strangers.

"Sure as could be, the younger and more aggressive of the two said, 'We've talked long enough. We don't want just directions, we want your money as well.' When he said that, I didn't hesitate. I pulled back the blanket and fired point blank at his right shoulder because he had his pistol and holster on the right side. They were only eight or ten feet away from the wagon and I couldn't miss.

"The bullet tore into his shoulder and he fell forward onto his horse and started screaming in pain. The horse took off with him riding in pain, holding his arm and not holding the reins; I could just imagine what that's going to end like. The other man started to draw his weapon. I just dropped him right from the saddle to the ground. One shot, he never moved. I told Tom to keep driving but to hasten a bit to Rollins; at that point it was just a mile or so away, as we were told by the wagon master when we split off from them.

"Tom said, 'Rosie, you are so good with that gun, why don't we make some money in the next town?'

"'What do you mean? What do you have in mind? It's not robbery, is it? I don't want to be a Belle Starr,' I said."

"'Let me take care of that. Just be ready to shoot for your supper and hopefully mine as well.' And he laughed for the next mile.

An illustration of Belle Starr being chased by National Police-1888

"We saw the sign as we entered the town 'Rollins, population 200.' It was a charming looking town with several houses on the main street with white picket fences and rosebushes in the yard. I was impressed because I hadn't seen flowers in a yard in over two weeks during this beautiful spring of 1901.

"Going down Main Street, looking at the nice little shops on each side, I didn't notice when Tom pulled the wagon right up to the front of Hotel Isabella DeRosa, a huge two-story white building with people going in and out of a large ornate glass front door.

"'Rosie, this is a real Victorian Hotel. You should perform for the good people of Rollins right here. Come, Rosie,' Tom said in a very loud voice I had never heard come from him since I had known him; he sounded like a circus leader.

"Tom climbed down from the wagon and took four coins from his pocket. A group of people gathered quickly to see what the loud voice and talk was all about. Before anyone could protest, Tom said, 'Rosie, this small coin is a quarter. Show the good people of Rollins how well you shoot. When I toss this coin into the air you draw and fire.'

"About that time, he runs about one hundred feet down the middle of the street, stops, turns, and throws a coin as far into the air as he could. With little or no effort, I pulled Nell from my holster and fired without aiming, knocking the coin from the air. Tom picks it up and shows the coin with a big hole right in the middle, and says, 'Rosie, put Nell away again. This time I'm going to toss these remaining three coins left in my hand into the air at the same time. Show the good folks what you can do with these coins.'

"I just stood there waiting for him to toss them. He whirled his body around, and at the same time released the coins so they flew into the air at different times and heights. As he did, he stumbled, nearly falling to the ground.

"I drew and fired three shots in a sequence. All three were dead-on hits through the coins. The people cheered and clapped like at a circus. Who would have thought it? I couldn't even believe it. Tom had drawn a crowd of people with hardly any effort. Tom picked up the coins, handed each one out to the several children there with their parents.

"I asked Tom, 'Now what?'

"Within minutes, several men came to Tom, not me, asking if they could get a photograph! Tom said, 'Let's pass the hat for this young lady. She has shown us shooting like no one since Annie Oakley.' Tom took off his tan cowboy hat that he had bought in Cheyenne and handed it to the man that had asked for the photograph."

"The man brought back the hat full of money. We counted over ten dollars in just five minutes of shooting. That started the sideshow of 'Rambling Rosie Runyon', a name Tom gave me that afternoon in Rollins, Montana.

A copy of the coin Rosie shot in several towns

"Of course, I had never showed off my shooting skills before because my father had said that he wanted me to only use the skill when needed for protection. In Tom's opinion, it was for protection, 'Protection from starvation, disregard and contempt of those God-given talents you honed for years. We are going to use your talents to get us across this country and maybe further,' Tom said with a smile, as we went into the hotel."

"Rock Springs, Idaho, was the next town we stopped that seemed big enough to draw a crowd. This show Tom had put together with the coins turned out perfect. It was so easy for me, and it was only a one-dollar investment of our time. Again, we had several men come to Tom and ask him if I would like to join a traveling show, with me as the star, shooting different targets.

Photograph taken of Tom in Rollins after the show

"'Do you want to do this, Rosie? You could be another Annie Oakley. I'm not sure, it would mean we would have to go when, where, and how the show owners wanted us to. After we signed a contract, we, but especially you, would be their property,' Tom said.

"'I didn't want to do this in the first place,' I told Tom. 'I'm doing it just because you seem to think it's a good way to make money while driving this wagon across the country. I know it keeps from digging into our little bankroll.' We decided to sleep on it that night and decide at breakfast while we were at the local hotel there in Rock Springs.

"The next morning Tom came down first while I tidied up. He ordered our breakfast and was sitting there reading the San Francisco newspaper when I came down.

While we were sitting at breakfast, another couple came down to eat with two small children; they were about two or three years of age. We heard them ask the cook if he knew where they could buy a horse and wagon to travel from Rock Springs due north about twenty miles where they had bought a homestead. 'We just got off the train here and have no means of transportation for our belongings. We have small children so we can't just ride two horses,' the lady said to the cook and waiter.

"I didn't realize Tom was listening to her. Tom put his newspaper down and walked over to her table. He put his hand out to shake the man's hand and said, 'I just may be able to help you folks out. I just overheard you asking about a wagon. We have a team and a wagon that we got from the Southern Pacific Railway when we ran into unforeseen track damage around Cheyenne a few weeks ago. I'm Tom Smith, and this is my wife, Rosie. We are on our way to the Yukon Territory and will be hopefully getting the train from here. Did your family travel from the west coast or close by?' as Tom pulled his chair over to their table without an invitation.

"We sat there and had breakfast and coffee with those folks, Lucy and Ronnie Collins. They gave us twenty-five dollars and promised to drop us off at the train station around noon that day for the train west.

"We then bought a ticket to the town of Seattle. We had picked up another railroad spur built from Idaho to the state of Washington. I thought we would have to go to San Francisco, but the conductor told us this would save us time, money and distance if we were going to the Klondike country.

"I noticed the people getting on and off the train didn't seem to be business people. The more north we went they were, let's say, unsavory types getting on board. I saw with my own eyes several ladies that up and pick-pocketed people as they came on board. Then there was another lady that carried her six-gun right like the cowboys we just left in Idaho, but the conductor either didn't see her or was afraid to confront her.

Work Locomotive going to Idaho

"It seemed to be a little more progressive, more lights and people, as we approached Seattle. We spent over a month getting from Cincinnati to Seattle. I had learned a little about Tom and a lot about traveling on this journey, and we weren't there yet."

Chapter 4

"We are all visitors to this time, this place.
We are just passing through.
Our purpose here is to observe, to learn, to grow, to love…
and then return Home."

Cherokee Saying

Grandma Rosie Continues to Tell About Their Trip West to the Yukon

We got to the Yukon Territory nearly two weeks later by rail spur and wagon just recently opened from Skagway. Tom asked the train conductor where most of the exploits had been for the gold. 'Most say up toward Minot, Dry Gulch, White Horse and Dawson City. You might want to choose Dawson City, a town of about one hundred miners usually but recently expanded to nearly 100,000 of all types that were there to "dig for gold" one way or the other. Thankfully, most now have cleared out to give Nome their trouble.' And he laughed.

"Tom said to the station conductor, 'We have traveled almost to the west coast eating dust, trekking across mosquito-infested bogs, on boats and now we're going to challenge the glaciers. But took this new spur up here into British Columbia, a shortcut of several hundred miles not on the original railroad map I looked at in the Norfolk-Western headquarters; it showed incomplete lines. I thought they would have been finished by this time.'

"'I think the Canadian Railway just finished it six or eight months ago, and that's why it was not on the main map. We have topical maps of the entire European system, Canadian system and United States system; they are loosely tied together somehow, aren't they?' the conductor asked, with a strange look on his face like he had never answered a question like that before. 'That information is way above my pay grade,' the conductor added with a smile.

"The station conductor said, 'Come with me. I'll get you to the spur that goes up that way. Are you sure you want this young lady to accompany you up there? It gets pretty rough up that way with all the miners and all that goes with gold fever: fast money, women, sin galore, lots to be made and lots to be lost in a short time, but suit yourself.'

"Tom said, 'Rosie's come this far; you aren't about to stop her now when just a day or two away.'

"'That's right. I think I can handle most things that come my way. If not, I have Nell with me to help,' and I pulled my coat back to show my Colt .45.

"The conductor said, 'I see you are going up there prepared for bear.'

"I said, 'You got that right.'"

Dawson City

"My first impression of the town wasn't much. The roads were muddy, ruddy and some of the worst I had ever seen, even worse than Virginia. The railroad station was no more than a shed the size of an outhouse where a man sold tickets. All the baggage was piled on a big wooden platform beside the ticket shed. It opened at six and closed at six in the evening; there was only one train each day going and coming.

"Tom had two large leather bags he would have to carry the half-mile into town himself, the ticket master told us. There was no transportation other than horses, wagons and a few mules that I could see, so we decided to walk. Everyone we passed on the road to town was either carrying a rifle or a pistol.

"We had walked about two hundred yards and Tom needed a break, so he set the bags down. When he did, I set my bag down and shifted Nell and strapped the holster to my right side. I had learned from Jake to shoot with either hand from either side, but from the right side I had a mite faster draw than the left, Jake had said.

"Anyway, we had only stood there resting for a few minutes in the warm sunshine when two horsemen came riding up at a good fast gallop. All of a sudden one jumps off his horse and grabs Tom without a word, other than 'Give me your money you...', and he used a profane slang. When that happened, I pulled Nell and fired one time, knocking his hat off. 'The next shot will be a little more painful,' I said to him. With that, his partner took off.

43

"He didn't want any part of us then. Not expecting such an event, Tom had been taken by surprise. But when he gathered his balance of his big six-foot two-inch, two-hundred-pound frame, he knocked the guy right off his feet. The guy grabbed his jaw and crawled away, then called his horse and rode off after his friend.

"'Well, Rosie, I'm damn glad you brought Nell. If those two were part of the welcoming committee, I can't wait to meet the other folks,' he said, with a look on his face I had not seen before as he picked up his hat and the two leather bags.

"'Yes, Nell is going to be close at hand the next few days, it looks. I hate to say it, but the folks up here don't seem a bit friendly. Maybe it's just that they can tell we're from back East,' I told Tom.

"We got into town without further incident. On first view it looked pretty rough—four streets I could count, one in each direction east, west, north and south. They were all pitted, rough and bumpy from dried mud. Each street was marked with a big wooden sign with a name, then the mileage in kilometers, which meant nothing to me.

"Tom was looking for a land office to see if we could get a small cabin or room without staying at the local hotel. 'Look, there it is in big red letters "Klondike Land Office" right beside the telegraph office. Let's walk over there and see if we can strike a deal on a place.'

A notice we saw at the Telegraph Office

"On the way to the land office we saw the telegraph office; there was a big board in the front displaying reward posters. We just stopped for a minute and counted 18 different wanted posters, and two were women!

"'Tom, what are you going to do in the land office?' I asked him.

"'Watch and listen. My father was always dealing in land. He would say, "God ain't makin' any more land, people are always wanting to buy or sell if the money is right." Well, I've only done a few land deals with him but when I told him I was coming up here he said, "Be sure to check out the land prices first, there may be more money there in property than in the gold in them there hills.'" And he laughed.

"When we got to the office, there were three men working, doing some type of bookwork. We set our bags down by the door. Tom walked right up to the window just like he knew something they didn't, and they may

45

want to ask him about it. They looked up at Tom, because he was so tall, I suppose.

"'What is the land availability here a mile or two out of town? I prefer to purchase but if need be, I can rent or lease for a few months. I'm with the Canadian Railroad, and we are looking for land to build a spur off the track outside of town, just speculation mind you,' Tom said, with a very authoritative voice.

"'Well, Mister, what did you say your name was?'

"'I didn't, but it is Tom Smith, sir.'

"'Mister Smith, how much land were you looking for? Is the land requirement several acres or smaller?'

"'Oh, usually about 5 acres, give or take, until we can determine the precise route of the track,' Tom said sternly.

"'Mister Smith, there's several five-, ten- or fifteen-acre parcels available but they are not surveyed off yet, and that could take weeks or months to get done with the request for smaller plots of land that we have. Will you be staying in town?'

"'That depends on you, if you can get us a place until we work out a deal; a little house, cabin or room we can stay up to a month. The company is speculating now, I'm sure they'll want something they can consider soon,' Tom said, in a peculiar manner.

"'Mister Smith, we have a small cabin with a nice fireplace that just came open yesterday. Would you like to take a look at it today? One of us will drive you out in the

Benz motorcar from England, as soon as our boss returns.'

"'That sounds good. When do you think he will return?' Tom asked.

"'Mr. Erickson, our boss, said if he has to come live here in the Yukon with us heathen then he was going to bring his motorcar. Here, let us prepare you both a cup of coffee while you wait. It shouldn't be long. Rosie, would you like a seat and some coffee?'

"In about a half an hour, a huge middle-aged man with blond curly hair, beard and handlebar mustache came in the door with a bundle of papers rolled up like wallpaper many wealthy people use on the walls in their house. He sounded loud and rough, telling the other men what had to be done right away. When he opened the rolled paper, Tom said later, they were blueprints that showed where claims were, and the next claim being staked in red.

"Soon, the man Tom had been talking to, introduced Tom, and told the boss, Erickson, why we were there and what had transpired. Erickson seemed to settle down to a normal pace instead of stamping around like a caged bull after that. My first impression, Erickson appeared as a big picaresque character.

"'Mr. Smith, you are a land speculator for the Canadian Railroad, and maybe interested in a five- or ten-acre plot for the railroad. Right now, you need a house or a place to lay your heads until we can get a suitable location for the railroad, is that correct?'

"'Yes, that is correct, sir,' Tom said.

"When Tom and Erickson were standing together, Erickson was more than three or four inches taller, and had to weigh close to 270 pounds. He made Tom look small and Tom usually made most other men look small.

"'Well, Tom, is this your beautiful wife?'

"'Yes. Erickson meet Ramblin' Rosie Runyon. A young lady I've been lucky enough to latch onto last year. We are looking for a place to settle down and start a family but thought we would come up here to the Yukon to see what this gold rush fever is all about while we were still young and would like some adventure in our life. I know getting rich quick is the central theme here, but there are a lot of ways money can be made rather than digging in the dirt for the gold, as many of the women up here can attest, I'm sure,' Tom exclaimed.

"It was then I knew what a wonderful man I had, with a gift of gab, as my father used to say. He could go into a complete room of strangers and feed them a load of bull hockey while they just stood around listening for more!

"As we walked out the door to go look at the property, I saw this thing pulled up to where the hitching post usually is for the horses. Tom exclaimed, 'This is the first real motorcar I have actually seen up close. My father saw a few in Washington, D.C., and New York City, but there were none in our area of Kentucky or Virginia.'

"Erickson answered with a proud statement, 'I told the mining company if they wanted me to come all the way over here to America, they would have to give me an extraordinary bonus. It took them several months to come up with something, but finally the company president came to me with this offer from the Benz Motor Company in Germany. It is about two years old now but when we have to go in the field it's very efficient for carrying equipment and survey instruments. As you can see, it sits two in the back and the driver sits in the fore seat. Jump in, we'll ride out to the Halstead cabin.'

"On the way out to the cabin property, I didn't say anything but I was probably as tickled as I was when I got to ride in Tom's steam engine locomotive for the first time a few years ago.

"'This is classy, wouldn't you say, Rosie?' Tom repeated several times, as we rode down the rutty road at a runner's pace. I was still not convinced that a horse and wagon wasn't better, but that may have been because I like horses a lot more than that crazy contraption they brought from overseas. It did go pretty good, about like a good trot for Diablo or Paint."

Chapter 5

Our Little Cabin

Freshly planted garden, blossoms in the trees.
Insects flying in the air without a care, gathering like fleas.
Children playing hopscotch, kite tails in the sky. Bunnies in
the meadow, Bluebirds flying by. Raindrops on the tulips,
clover on the ground.
Blankets drying in the wind, very few women around.

- Rosie Runyon

Rosie and Tom Find A Home

While riding out to the cabin site, Tom asked Erickson, 'Does your family live here with you?'

"'God save the Queen; my wife and family are back in Great Britain. We have two children that are six and eight. I miss them terribly and have desired to get back to see them a year ago, but our company can't get anyone they can depend on to hold the fort down here for four weeks while I go back on holiday. It takes someone with broad shoulders in more ways than physical and mental; a great deal of responsibility goes with this job,' Erickson said, in a disgustful way.

"'A bit further towards our destination and we'll be there. Tom, you seem to know a lot about land. You

51

wouldn't happen to be a surveyor, would you?'

"'Not really. I'm an engineer by trade, railway locomotive engineer most recently.'

"'What's a well-educated man like you and your beautiful bride, Rosie, doing up here in this gold rush country?' Erickson said, in his heavy foreign accent.

"'Rosie and I felt we needed a little adventure together while we are still young, and before we start our brood. I'm a little older than Rosie and traveled extensively as a student in the eastern United States, but nothing like we have done so far coming here to the west coast and Canada. When Rosie read about the gold rush up here in the Yukon, we thought *why not go take a look for ourselves?* Why do you ask?'

"'You fit the bill of what our company is looking for in terms of an employee to temporarily run this place until I can take a trip to England for a month or two. There is one thing I would need to know. Do you ride and shoot? You are well educated, big and strong looking, but can you fight? You know there has been almost a killing each day here in this small place, more than the city of London. O' bloody hell, we are here. We can talk about work at a later time. You both want to see the place, I'm sure,' Erickson said, with a little excitement in his voice.

"We got out of the one-time shiny Benz motorcar and followed Erickson to a little log cabin. The cabin was almost two miles out of town on a partially wooded mountainside two-acre plot, just between two mountain ranges, with a beautiful view of another mountain range on the horizon. It had a little running brook just behind the house about fifty feet down a little embankment.

The little cabin in the Yukon Territory

"Erickson said, 'It is fishable most of the year when it's not frozen over. It has a nice big fireplace with three glass windows, one on each side of the great room and one in the back. The best thing about the cabin, I think, is it has a wine cellar. Of course, they call it a basement. There's possible electric and telegraph poles available down the road a mile or so in the coming future.

"'Right now, only oil lamps and candles for you here,' Erickson emphasized.

"'It will be twenty dollars each month or three hundred dollars to buy. Go in and see if you can live there. A husband and wife just had it while they were in Dawson. He struck gold on a claim about a mile north of here and made more than a thousand dollars. They left the next week and sold us back the claim and the cabin.'

"None of that seemed to bother Tom as we talked about the cabin. He was busy taking measurements, testing the bedframe, and noticing what went with the property.

"'What is your feeling, Tom? Do you want to take it for a month or two or try to find something in town?'

"He looked at Erickson. 'We'll take it, if Rosie likes it. Seems just like your kind of place, Rosie! We will know in a month or two if we want to stay or not. It is now just the start of July, Erickson. We'll give you twenty now and twenty each month until the company decides on the land.'

"Later, after Erickson left, I asked, 'What's the deal with telling them you work for Canadian Railroad and they are looking for land up here to build a railway exchange spur? You're not with the Canadian Railway.'

"'I simply embellished a little. My boss told me the Canadian Railway was so overextended it would be a year getting rail service to this point north. They were more interested in the westward expansion than the northward expansion. Anyway, I thought I could use that as a handle with the land office for a few weeks until we decided what we want to do. At least it got us this little cabin, didn't it?'

"'Yes, I guess it did.' I had to give Tom credit that his gift of gab has helped us all along the way. I am a

Philomath, Tom said, and laughed at whatever that was. He was always coming up with these terms I hadn't heard of, so that day I asked him where they came from. He said they are Latin, a language that was used many years ago. I just let it go at that; I didn't feel like discussing something that wasn't even used anymore. Now I'm a Philomath, what the hell else is he going to lay on me?

"'When we go back into town, we'll get this all down on paper with Erickson. Rosie, you want to stay here and look around. I'm going outside to see what we have around the cabin and how the stream runs in the middle of summer. Isn't this a beautiful vista from up here in the mountains? A lot different than the old hills of the Appalachians. These are real mountains, Rosie. We can go climbing, hunting, fishing, and hiking, about anything we can think of up here.' Tom was still talking to himself as he closed the back door of the cabin to explore our new home."

Chapter 6

"The earth has music for those that listen."
-William Shakespeare

Victoria

After we secured the cabin, we had shelter, water and heat. We then decided the next need was transportation. We were nearly two miles from town; normally, that would be nothing to walk but here walking was another matter. Like we saw on our first day of arrival it could be a challenge.

"I decided we needed a mule rather than a horse. I had seen how valuable a mule is when I was a child around the farm. You might say here it is the difference in riding need. This was the type of terrain where one needed a mule. Something hardy and strong. My daddy had several mules he could depend on in any weather, day or night, working the fields plowing or clearing timber. My father the 'Horse Man' would say, 'I will put my mule up against any horse when it comes to work. Running and racing, well now, that's another matter altogether.'

"Tom said, 'Rosie, this is your department. I'll go into town and get whatever you say.'

"'I think we need a small wagon, like a buckboard, and a mule. Go to a blacksmith and ask him to advise you on

57

the purchase of a small wagon a mule can hitch to, and a mule that has been trained to pull a wagon, as well as to ride if or when we want. I know they will try to sell you a horse but don't listen to the bull. They'll tell you about how much better a horse and wagon will be for your needs. Ah hell, do you want me to go get them, Tom?' I asked him.

"I pulled a pair of bib-overalls from my bag, got out of my long gingham blue dress and put on a red flannel shirt of Tom's. Plus, I had worn my old brogans from back home; as a result, my feet were comfortable most of the time.

"'Damn, Rosie, you could pass for a right pretty man.'

"'That's the idea, Tom. If I'm walking into town, I'll have far less trouble as a man than if they think I'm a woman,' I explained to him. 'I even have your old railroad handkerchief and hat you gave me over a year ago, to wipe the grease off my hands and to keep the coal dust out of my hair. I never returned them because they were so sentimental to me. Plus, they came in handy so many times since then.'

"'Damn, I still can't believe my eyes; you are such a pretty man, I may be tempted.' And he laughed like hell.

"I punched him hard right in the chest; that made him laugh harder. Then I told him I needed twenty-five dollars, and he suddenly stopped laughing.

"'Really? That much?'

"'Yep. A horse and wagon would cost us even more.'

Tom and I kissed. I didn't think I'd be back until way past evening, I told him. Then I set out for town walking, and was passed by only a few riders that didn't even give me a second glance.

"I was about a mile from the cabin when a dark-faced woman with a horse and wagon asked me if I wanted a ride. She was alone in an open buckboard, something like I was looking for us to buy. Before I accepted the ride, I asked her how she knew from the back I was a woman walking.

"'That would be easy, my dear. I'm a veterinarian, a horse doctor from Scotland, and each species–male and female–have a way of walking. Haven't you noticed a difference in the prance of a stud and a mare?' she asked, as I climbed aboard.

"'Yes, I have, but never thought about it for men and women. Although now that you mention it, I have seen women that have a sway to their walk that causes men to turn their heads.'

"'Well, yes, it is the same with men and women regardless how they think; their pelvis is built differently, your anatomy determines the movement,' she said, in a very teacher-type voice.

"'What is anatomy? I think I know but just to listen to you explain it will be an education for me.'

"Victoria laughed when I said that, then I heard her say 'giddy up' to her horse. I knew then she wasn't too foreign.

"'You are dark. Does your family live here or in town?' I said to her, as I looked at her rig. The harness was light leather but looked rugged and sturdy. The rig was well built but a lighter wood than we used on the farm; just the type I wanted to go back and forth into town to carry groceries, clothes and farm equipment.

"'Yes, my father is from Egypt, in north Africa. My mother is French, but she moved with her family to Egypt. They met and got married. They moved to Scotland when I was very young, for a job for my father.

"'My family came to Ottawa, Canada, over ten years ago again for work but kept moving west every few years. My family moved what seemed like every two or three years. I didn't understand why until I finally got out of the Catholic school system.

"'They say that people in the South hate dark folks like me. If it's any worse than up here, it must be terrible to be black in the South. I went to the University of Quebec and decided animals are color blind to the human. I have been fine ever since. You seem different, not pre-judgmental like some folks,' Victoria said, very eloquently.

"'I'm not sure what that big word is but I have a feeling, and you're right, I'm not. To me each person earns their right to be treated equally by the way they treat people. My mother taught us to treat everyone as we would like to be treated. I've always tried to do that, regardless,' I told her. 'Aren't you afraid to ride the roads alone?' I asked Victoria.

"'Sometimes there is the occasional problem,' and she kicked a horse blanket off a sweet little .30-30. 'There's a pistol I keep in my doctor's bag over there. It is a big black leather bag, since all my instruments are large for the horses, cows, sheep and other animals,' she said.

"'I like your Colt .45 you are carrying, with those white pearl handles. Can you use it, or do you just carry it to scare off the possible troublemakers?'

"I admitted to her that I was a pretty good shot. 'See that bird flying up ahead?' I drew and fired one shot. The poor bird dropped a little less than a hundred yards ahead.

"'Lordy, Miss, you can shoot. I needed your skill several times but just kept shooting until I thought I hit what I was amin' at. Usually, I was successful but there have been times…well let's just say I wasn't successful. I'll tell you about that some other time; we are just about in town. Where are you going to do your business? I'll drop you," Victoria said, in a very Scottish accent.

"'I'm going to buy a mule and wagon. Me and my husband just moved to town and we need them for transportation. Is there a blacksmith you can show me to?'

"'You are in luck; I know the blacksmith pretty well. We have helped each other a great deal. I'll vouch for you if you need me to. I'll take you there; it's just up the street.'

"'It probably wouldn't hurt, if you have the time. It will hurry things along; that way I can get back to the cabin before dark,' I told her.

"'You know, I live about another mile past you, if you have that little cabin by the creek that has just gone empty the last week or so. If for some reason you can't strike a deal with Luscious Jameson, the blacksmith, just walk up to the general store about fifty yards north and tell the store keep you are Rosie Smith, waiting for Victoria the Vet. Many in town call me VV, for short. They will look out for you until I get back this way in the afternoon.

"'If you do strike a deal, go to the store anyway. Open a charge account for groceries this winter. You'll be glad you did. Sometimes we get snowed in for a week or more, and a few more groceries really come in handy.'

"'Honest, Victoria, you have been a great help, an absolute brick already. I'd like to see you again. I've got a lot on my plate until we get settled but after that I would like to get together with you for coffee or tea. I make some mighty good biscuits with apple butter we can snack on while we talk.'

"'That sounds like a splendid deal. Here's the livery stable and the blacksmith right here together. Come on, I have time to introduce you.'"

Victoria the Vet

Chapter 7

*Never be a prisoner of your past. It was just a lesson,
not a life sentence.*

Old Fred

That'sthe way I was introduced to a fine lady and somewhat of a partner in thought and practice. It was unusual to find a woman who was a professional and stood up for what she believed. I liked her from the very beginning I knew we had a common bond. I didn't care what color she was to me. You 'can't judge a book by its cover', as my mother used to say.

"Mr. Luscious Jameson was a big, gruff Swedish man who had a quite manner to go with the blond hair, blue eyes, and fair skin. Just what you would think of when you think of the Swede population. He was friendly, especially with Doctor VV, as he called her. He wanted $25 for each, the wagon and the mule; but Victoria wore Luscious down to the $20 price range, then handed him over to me.

"I finally got the mule, 'Old Fred,' and one fine little wagon to go with him for $20 because I was a friend of Victoria's. I went over to the general store and bought two weeks' worth of food, garden hoe, shovel, ax, lamps, lamp oil, candles, mirror, soap, and a few more things for me and Tom. Then drove home with my new wagon with Old

Fred the mule I was introduced to that day.

"Tom and I worked like hell the next two weeks getting the place fixed like we wanted. I worked inside the cabin and Tom worked outside. I didn't realize what a good worker Tom was, but he fixed shutters for the windows, bolted the door, and hoed out a little garden patch for some late vegetables beside the house.

"Tom came in, excited to let me know he had put the new hoe to use that I had purchased at the general store. 'Rosie, you would not believe how nice this soil is up here. I want to plant a little garden. Will you get the seeds and plants when Mr. Jameson gets them in?'

"'Sure, Tom,' I reassured him.

"Our nearest neighbor, an old Swedish couple, was one and half miles to the north. They had more than a hundred acres between us, we're told at the general store. Tom and I rode over to their place one day to ask them where the head of the stream was located, as an excuse to meet them.

"Roland and Matilda were their names, as we introduced ourselves. They invited us in for coffee and were ever-so-friendly. Come to find out they had lived there for the past forty years and practically built the town of Dawson. Matilda wanted me to see her house trappings of pictures, novelties and cookware she had collected over the years. Of course, I was courteous and accommodated her.

"When Tom asked Roland about his background,

Roland said, 'I was a timber man and my three sons are all lumberjacks and carpenters; they literally built the town over the last thirty years. Matilda and I are both in our late eighties, and don't do much anymore except try to keep this farm going. But let me take you to the head of the stream while the women are jawing.'

"Tom said they got on Roland's adapted steam wagon because he was too old and unsteady to walk a distance anymore. This steam engine pulled the wagon instead of a mule or horses. They slowly rode for almost half an hour through densely wooded forest, up and down the mountainside, until they finally stopped at a clearing with a beautiful lake covering an estimated five acres.

Photo of 1898 steam tractor

"'This is it!' Roland said, as they got off his land steam engine. 'This is the head of the little creek that runs past your cabin. It is approximately a half mile by the crow but with all the twist and turns in the stream it's more like a mile. I've stocked the lake here three times in the past twenty-five years, so I know by now there's some good fishing in there. Come on up and throw in a hook, see what you can pull out when you and Rosie get a chance.'

"They walked the area and he told Tom, 'This is the head of the stream and my original spot picked out to build on. However, after we got the sawmill started, the boys were born and then time just slipped by, and building up here never happened. This is the northwestern corner of my property,' Roland told Tom. 'Both of my boys selected ten acres on the south side. Lorrain, our daughter, married and took off to Calgary with her new man; they've started a family down there. As a result, this wonderful piece of property is still sitting here, untouched for over fifty years now.'

"Tom explained to Mr. Sorenson, 'This is a great piece of property. I would love to have enough money to make you a good offer for the land, but my wife and I just moved here. We haven't decided if we are going to stay yet. Let me tell her about the land, bring her up here, show her the potential, then we can decide.'

"'That sounds fair. Maybe my wife and I can have you two over for dinner one evening before the weather gets bad. By the end of October, it can get pretty bad and the days are awfully short,' Roland said, with a blank stare at the lake.

"'Shall we get back?' Tom asked Roland, since he was just standing there looking at the lake like his mind was far away in another place.

"'Will we get like that, Rosie?' Tom asked on our ride back home. We discussed the beautiful land and lake he showed Tom but that was just too much to consider at the present time for us. This little cabin was just enough at the moment.

"'I'm not sure, but most of my folks have been up near ninety before they have started to mentally slip,' I told him. 'I have a lot of Cherokee blood because my grandmother was captured by a Cherokee tribal chief by the name of Matuka. They took her, and she had at least two children by him. I don't know specifics, because no one in the family wanted to spill the beans that would explain the details. The other side of the coin is our entire bloodline now partly belongs to the Cherokee tribe.

"'Because of that, Sarah and me was invited to the tribe at the age of twelve to study to be a midwife for women in need, and herbal medicine with the tribal medicine man. It was his feeling if you did many of the things the white man does it will shorten one's life; like firewater, tobacco, staying up at night; Cherokees go to bed shortly after the sun goes down. Eating the wrong kind of food is another problem the white man does not understand. We studied different herbs to help conditions and injuries the warriors used to get during battle, even during sickness.'

'I wasn't sure about all those things until I got a little older; now I can see the relations of those influences on a person's health even more.

"'That's what I want to talk to Victoria about. Maybe

Some tribes marked their captors like Olive Oatman at 14

she can give some light on what she does with injury and sickness with animals. Most people only care about their horses, but other people have said they own other animals they care about as well. I agree. Really can't see much difference with humans and animals other than size, yet they have somehow kept more hair than we humans have,' I told Tom with a big grin.

"'Dang it, Rosie, I never thought about it but I think you are right. I know my father thought that animals rarely got sick until they eat human food. Then they get some of the same conditions humans get,' Tom said, with a surprised look on his face like he had never thought about it in detail before.

"That evening we sat down at our old wooden table,

said grace over our simple meal of fresh fish, greens, and tomatoes by oil lamp. Tom said, 'This meal is pure ambrosia. You know how to make the simplest pleasures delightful. A few wildflowers, a checkered tablecloth; if we only had music, it would be like a table in New York City.'

"'Well, Tom, thank you, I couldn't bring my banjo, or we could have added the music.'

"'Just think, all of this without potation involved! Who would have thunk it?' he said to me with a smile. He had a romantic notion I wasn't aware of until after dinner.

In the words of Rosie Runyon:

"Nature provides us with everything we need in order to survive, and there are a few wild plants that are commonly used as first aid. These wild healing plants are well-known by the Native Americans for their healing properties. Those people living off the land have been using them for more than a hundred years before me.

"If you get stranded in the wild or if you plan to live off the land, learn how to find the following essential wild healing plants. You could use them until professional medical help would be available. Some of these wild healing plants are already available in your garden or living area. Most people see them only as invasive weeds, without having a clue about their healing benefits," Grandma stated.

Take a look at a few that Grandma Rosie suggests keeping around for their medicinal benefits.

This plant has been used for centuries across North American and Europe and it is widely spread across the country. Nettles are known to treat allergies, anemia, arthritis, bronchitis, burns and scalds, fatigue, internal bleeding, kidney stones, parasites, poor circulation, pre-menstrual syndrome, urinary tract infections, and more. Because of its many nutrients, stinging nettle is traditionally used as a spring tonic.

It is a slow-acting nutritive herb that gently cleanses the body of metabolic wastes. As a diuretic, stinging nettle increases the secretion and flow of urine. This makes it invaluable in cases of fluid retention and bladder infections. It is also anti-lithic, breaking down stones in the kidneys and gravel in the bladder. When it comes to wild healing plants, stinging nettle stands out due to its many uses.

Nettle (Stinging Nettle)

Besides being a good edible plant, it can also be used to make cordage, and bring feeling back to frozen hands and feet. Europeans and Native Americans have used the fibers from stinging nettle to make sailcloth, sacking, cordage, and fishing nets.

If you would like to use nettles for food or tea, you need to harvest the plants before they flower. Otherwise, you can harvest stinging nettle from the time the new leaves emerge until late fall when the flowers have gone to seed.

Plantain

Considered a garden weed in many parts of North America, plantain is one of the most powerful wild healing plants. Even more, plantain is an edible plant that can be foraged in both wild and urban environments. Plantain is originally native to Europe, and today it can be found in many parts of North America.

Believed to have been brought to the Americas by the Puritans, plantain was referred to as "white man's footprint" among some Native American tribes because of how it well it thrived in the disturbed areas surrounding European settlements.

The first pioneers, due to its natural antibacterial and anti-inflammatory properties, used plantain. It is of great use when it comes to speeding recovery of wounds, and for itching or pain associated with skin problems. Externally, plantain has been used for insect and snakebites, and as a remedy for rashes and cuts.

Yarrow

This plant grows wild all across the United States and it was one of the wild healing plants used by the Native Americans tribes. It was known and appreciated for its highly antimicrobial and anti-infectious properties. Ancient Greeks first used yarrow over 3,000 years ago for treating external wounds on the skin to slow down bleeding. The flowers and leaves of yarrow were eaten and also made into a tea-like drink.

Yarrow leaves can be used raw or cooked. Although they have a bitter flavor, you can use them in mixed salads and are best used when the leaves are young. The entire plant can be used, both dried and fresh, and it is recommended to gather it while in flower. Fresh leaves can be used to treat gastrointestinal problems, fight fevers, lessen menstrual bleeding and improve circulation. You can also make a tincture or poultice to treat rashes and broken skin.

Common Mallow

This plant is considered an invasive weed in the United States. However, it's also appreciated for its wide range of medicinal and food uses. It is one of the wild healing plants that can be used completely. Each part of the plant has specific uses. The leaves, flowers, seedpods and roots can be used for both food and medicine.

Common mallow leaves and young shoots of common mallow are edible raw or cooked. Immature seeds are also edible raw or cooked and they contain 21% protein and 15.2% fat. All parts of common mallow are astringent, laxative, urine inducing, and have agents that counteract inflammation, that soften and soothe the skin when applied locally, and that induce the removal of mucous secretions from the lungs.

Due to its astringent, bactericidal and anti-inflammatory properties, common mallow can be used externally as an herbal treatment for wounds, skin rashes, insect bites and swellings. This plant is highly appreciated in the Jewish culture as it played an important role as famine crop during the siege of Jerusalem in 1948. Survivalists often use the roots of common mallow as a toothbrush replacement. Homesteaders used to make cream, yellow and green dyes, by using this plant.

Burdock

Although Burdock is native to Europe and Northern Asia, thanks to the first settlers this plant is now widespread throughout the United States where it is seen as a weed. It is one of the wild healing plants that were widely used as a food source in Europe, but also for its medicinal properties.

The root, herb and seeds can be used, and you need to learn when to harvest them. With little effort, the roots can be dug in July. They are about 12 inches in length and about 1 inch thick and are hard to miss. The leaves can also be collected in July, but the seeds should be collected when ripe in the fall. Young burdock roots, flower stems and even very young leaves are consumed eagerly in many parts of Asia and Europe. To remove the bitter taste of the roots, slice them thinly and soak them in water with a little apple cider vinegar for a few hours.

When it comes to its healing properties, the root is principally employed, but the leaves and seeds are equally valuable. You can make a decoction using both root and seeds. Its anti-scorbutic properties will help heal boils, scurvy and rheumatic affections. An infusion of the leaves is useful to impart strength and tone to the stomach, and some forms of long-standing indigestion. When applied externally as a poultice, the leaves are highly efficient for some tumors and gouty swellings. It generally relieves bruises and inflamed surface areas.

Dandelion

The common dandelion is also known as: Puffball, Blow ball, Canker wort, Irish daisy and Priest's crown. Its botanical name is Taraxacum officinale. You may be most familiar with dandelion as a stubborn weed that never seems to leave your lawn or garden. However, in traditional herbal medicine practices, dandelions are revered for their wide array of medicinal properties. For centuries, they've been used to treat a myriad of physical ailments, including cancer, acne, liver disease and digestive disorders. Here are a few potential health benefits of dandelion, and what science has to say about them.

Author's note: My grandmother influenced me a great deal in the area of herbal medicine. She took me at age ten or eleven and would show me different wild greens, trees, fruits, nuts and explain the health benefit of each. When I was twelve, she showed me how herbs were identified and why they were good or bad for the body. This section of the book is important to point out the dried herbs Grandma Rosie carried in her carpet bag to the Yukon. There're also several references for further study on herbs some may find interesting. I found herbs, minerals, and vitamins very useful in my practice, especially for the elderly and infirm. During practice in the 1988 Olympic games in Seoul, Korea, I was amazed to find a very high percentage of the athletes were taking herbs, vitamins and minerals from their countries' local medicine men or acupuncturists. During lectures after the Olympic games, I found this to be true throughout the world.

Chapter 8

No poison can kill a positive thinker just as no medicine can save a negative thinker!

-Victoria Fukinbara (1901)

A Ride to the Badlands

N early a month had passed before I could find a chance to meet up with Victoria. Then we had coffee one morning at our little cabin while Tom rode into town to talk to Mr. Erickson at the land office about a job. Even though Tom didn't survey, he knew a great deal about land transactions and could certainly 'hold the fort down' for Erickson for a month or two when he needed a break to go see his wife, Tom thought.

"'Rosie, I'm intrigued as to why you two came out here to the Yukon without anyone to receive you or help you, all the way across country. That must have been a horrendous trip for you and Tom,' Victoria exclaimed.

"'Well, to tell you the truth we both figured we were going by train with Tom working for the railroad and all. I didn't think we would have to get a covered wagon dang near halfway across the country. Yet, it's no different than you coming all the way from Egypt or Scotland. I don't even know where that is, to tell you the truth, but I know they're across the ocean somewhere,' Rosie exclaimed.

81

"'Oh, I was actually born in Scotland, but we moved to Canada when I was about six. Tell you the truth, I'm not sure if my parents came here for work opportunity or running away from people in Scotland ostracizing them for being an interracial couple.'

"'You'll have to excuse my lack of education. I'm not sure of many of those terms but I think I know what you mean. The fact that your father and mother were different skin colors, I would imagine. People for the most part don't understand that color is only skin deep. Look at horses, dogs, rabbits; they may be the same breed but are often different colors.

"'The Indians took my grandmother many years ago and now we are a mixed family, so I know what you're going through. People for years tried to scorn our family, but my father wouldn't budge. He said, "I'm proud of my family heritage regardless of what they have had to endure. Yes, we are part Indian, European and I don't know what all, but we're American now!"

"'Speaking of the Indians, I wanted to ask you about your knowledge of herbal medicine. What do you use when a mother calf delivers her young, when her tits get a rash and inflamed easily?'

"'It's very different. It depends on the part of the country you are in. Some areas have good medication, like Vancouver and southern British Columbia; yet some have a scarcity of any medications for animals at all, like up here. So, I have learned to just tell the farmer, rancher or animal owner that no medication is available and go ahead with the procedure. Usually, that has worked out all right but there have been times, I'm sure, it would have helped to have something to reduce the inflammation,' Victoria said, in a nonpareil way.

"'What would you think if I rode along with you for a week or two in order to see if I think I can help in that way? I have helped my father deliver many animals, and I think the procedures and treatments we have used from the Indians have helped.

"'Besides, I'm a midwife, and in that area I know I can help. I've delivered or helped to deliver over twenty-five babies in the last few years. I know there's not going to be as many who want to start a family up here in the Yukon, but chances are it'll happen when they don't expect it. If it does, I'll be here to help!'

"'Damn, Rosie, I think you've hit upon something. We can have the first birth center, *Man or Beast,*' and Victoria started laughing. 'You can help me with the horses and cows, I'll help you with the women and children.' Her smile was enchanting, with beautiful teeth, smooth dark olive skin. It was nice to talk to a woman that understood my feeling.

"'I'm not joshing. I'm willing to help you even if you don't have the time to help me. I want to be able to do something up here in this new location besides knit, sew and play checkers in the winter. I hear the winter gets mighty long up here.'

"'That it does, Rosie. Some days it's ten to twelve

centimeters each snowfall and that can go on for weeks; the ground is frozen for months on end,' Victoria said in disgust.

"'Something I can't understand, Victoria. Why do you all say centimeters, and we say inches? It comes out the same. You'll have to help me with that one. My mother and father never explained that I would run into that one. Even our horses we measure in hands, and I heard them at the livery stable talking about centimeters. Well, anyway, I wanted a mule and when I finally got that across to Mr. Jameson it didn't matter about the hands or the centimeters. That's another thing I have to thank you for; you made that deal much easier than it was going to be, I'm sure.'

"'I'm going to have to be going. It's getting to be close to my next appointment. There is a mare having a foal about an hour north of here. It's real rough country up there, both geographically and physically. Most men up there don't want to fool with a black woman, won't even let their horses be treated. Yet some men just don't care, they would do it with a billy goat.' We laughed out loud again.

"'I'll tell you what, let me ride with you. I'll be able to see the countryside, meet a few people, plus, I might get a shot or two off to scare the birds away. Victoria, I'm not joshing now, I could ride shotgun if it's that rough up there. I would be happy to do it.'

"'I would much appreciate the company, and the added protection; up there you certainly need all you can get. They are even building a new Mounties Station up that way.'

"'How long do you think we'll be?' I asked her. 'I need to let Tom know where I've gone.'

"'An hour and a half each way and most of an hour there. That's four hours if we get started now.'

"'I'll leave Tom a note, since I have no way of contacting him. I'm sure it will be most of the day for him as well.' I scribbled a note on some paper we picked up the general store just for such purposes.

Dear Tom,

I have gone with Victoria to a farm north of here to help a mare deliver a foal. Be back as soon as possible.

Love, Rosie

"As we rode along, she told me how bad people had been to their family the first few years they were living here in Dawson City. 'However, when my father and I saved a woman's life the second year we were here at a local lake south of here where everyone went swimming, it all changed.

"'It was around the end of July or early August; about the only time the water is warm enough to go swimming. The town's people would usually move away from our family to the other end of the lake, until one day a little girl and her mother were wading in the lake. All of a sudden, the mother disappears, and the little girl started screaming. My father ran without hesitation toward the scream. We were at least a minute or two from them at running speed.

"'When my father jumped in to grab the lady, she was going down for the third time, her daughter said. My father pulled her out, pushed on her back for two or three minutes while others watched in amazement. A few minutes later she spit out a big gulp of water, then another, and another before she could breathe or talk.

"'To make a long story short, the woman and little girl were the family of a rich, local mine owner. After that incident, we no longer had to swim alone at the far end of the lake, as a matter of fact. The mine owner offered my father a big reward, but my father refused and told the man it was his humane duty, he would have done the same for anyone.

"'After that incident, our family was accepted to all the social functions of the village. That village status would soon change to Dawson City also, and it was soon to be flooded by gold seekers such as yourselves.'

"I said, 'Yes, I did read in an Ohio newspaper that thousands were rushing to the gold fields in the Yukon Territory to make their fortune, and many have, I'm told. Tom and I really didn't come here to seek a fortune or to dig gold for that matter. I just wanted to see what all the excitement was all about. Tom had a good job with the Norfolk & Western railroad as an engineer and I would have been happy to stay there in the hills of the Appalachian Mountains to start a family. But my sister urged me to get out and see the world while I was still young and could. That's really what caused me to yearn to ask Tom to go on a little adventure before we started a family. But now that I think about it, I would like to go in a gold mine or dig for gold, whatever way would be possible for me just for the experience.'

"'Here we are,' said Victoria, as we steered the team up this long, rough lane with potholes deep as craters. 'This rancher has fifty head of cows with three milk-giving; it was one of those that was in trouble the last time I was here, three months ago,' she said.

"The rancher, a tall, slender man about forty, with brown hair and a scruffy reddish beard, came out and told Victoria, 'The mare's been in labor for half the morning and maybe longer.' It seemed to him like she was not delivering properly but he had only seen two delivered before this one, and thought he better have Dr. Victoria there to assist and show him again the procedure.

"Victoria and I went to the barn with the rancher. This is where he kept his milk cows also because he had lost two heifers to wolves three weeks earlier this summer.

"'I didn't think this mare would have any problem because this is the third foal she's had. I stuck her in here with the milk cows to keep her protected as well.

"'I'm more worried to be down to two milk cows with winter coming on with a family of five to feed; it's not going to be easy if we lose another,' he stated.

"Victoria stooped down, put a long pair of rubber gloves on and started her procedure. In fifteen minutes, there was the foal's head; the problem was in the birth canal.

"'She was trying to deliver breech, or in other words, she was coming out backward,' Victoria said, 'I just reached in and offered a little assistance, and mother nature took over. That's what I love about my job, most of the time mother nature does the work.'

"'While you're here, doctor, would you be so kind as to take a quick look at this milk cow? Her udder is very red and sore, and if I can't get near her to milk, there will be a great deal of trouble. If I don't get her milked pretty soon, you know what that can cause.'

"'Sure, show her to me,' Victoria said.

"We walked out in a big open pasture where several cows were grazing. The rancher said, 'I'll have to run her down, she won't come in anymore for feed for fear that I will try to milk her.'

"We then went out to the corral where the farmer had a variety of livestock, horses, sheep, cows and even chickens running around. I noticed a pig pen about forty yards downwind. The farmer slowly walked up to a jersey cow. He reached down to show her udders, but she reluctantly pulled back. He finally had to take her leg and hold it while Victoria bent down to look. Two of her udders were red and swollen, it even looked sore to me.

"'See what I mean?' he said to Victoria.

"'Rosie, what would you suggest in a case like this?'

"'That's a good question. Most of my patrons can talk

and tell me what the problem is. Here you have a patron that you can see what the problem is, but she can't say anything in words. There is an old homemade remedy that a number of farmers use back home–they called it udder butter. You gently rub it on the swollen udders each day until the redness and swelling goes away. Since we don't have that available, you'll have to make your own.

"'Mr. Collins, you and your wife pick some burdock, mallow, yarrow and plantain leaves and roots. Those like I see growing around this corral can be used. Boil them together about thirty to forty-five minutes, until they soften, mash them up together until it becomes a thick, paste-like consistency. After it cools, rub some of this concoction on her udders each morning and evening for the next ten to fifteen days. After that she'll be back to herself. Keep these ingredients on hand to make.'

"'Save a vet bill for mastitis next time,' Victoria said with a laugh. Then I laughed to let him know we were joking.

"Mr. Collins was amazed and blurted out to us,

"'One more favor while you're here. My favorite plow horse has been limping around the last few days. Will you take a look at him before you leave?'

"He whistled and called for Thrasher, and the horse slowly limped over to us. Mr. Collins reached down and lifted the front leg. When he did, the horse tried to pull away. Mr. Collins gently talked to him and calmed him down.

"Victoria grabbed her bag and looked for a few

minutes, searching for the correct tool to use. Finally, she pulled out a large pair of what looked like tweezers. She gently lifted the horse's right front hoof, and when she did it was like the horse knew he was going to be helped. Victoria pulled a large piece of splintered wood from the hoof. She poured some alcohol on the area, wrapped the hoof in thick cheesecloth, with a thin piece of leather strapping over that to hold it in place.

"While she was standing there with the horse's hoof in her hands she said,

"'Mr. Collins, by the time he wears this cloth and leather a few days, the wound will be healed over, it'll be covered and protected during that time. He will be safe to use again to plow or ride after that time.'

"'I don't know where he could have picked up such a large wooden splinter, but that's neither here nor there now. I'm just happy he will be fine.'

"He took us into the house. His wife, a pretty young redhead with freckles and pigtails and two young children in tow, gave us some vittles packed into a cheesecloth to eat for the trip back home. He handed Victoria a few dollars and said, 'I'm sorry, I know this isn't as much as it should be, but I've hit a streak of bad luck. Don't worry, I'll make it up to you next time. Rosie, it was great meeting you. It looks like you two have a great one-two punch together on the animal care now, for sure.'

"Victoria said, 'Don't worry, Mr. Collins, what really counts is that all turned out like it should.' Victoria turned toward me and said, 'Let's ride, Rosie, I don't want nightfall to catch us.'

"With that, we got our jackets, watered and fed the team while we ate a few of the fixin's his wife had prepared for us just before we left for the long jaunt back to Dawson City."

Chapter 9

Don't tell people your plans, show them your results.
-Victoria (1901)

Why it was called Badlands

On the way back to Dawson, everything was going fine; we talked of why, when and where Victoria did each procedure. We both were familiar with each practice. It was the terminology that was different for each routine we had to get correct. We had been talking almost an hour about British veterinary medicine, my traditional folk medicine, and the Indian herbal procedures and how to utilize each of them, when all of a sudden there were gunshots coming from the hills somewhere around us.

"'It may be the Northwest Mounted Police after one of a gang supposedly staying in a hideout in the mountains toward Skagway. Rosie, have you seen the Mounted Police? They would want to take you with them as a recruit. They can shoot, ride, rope, and they are so good looking in their red uniforms. They have a headquarters up at the top of the mountain, somewhere between here and Dawson, but they are never where I need them for sure. Sometimes they are spotted in Dawson City at the courthouse or jail, bringing in someone for incarceration.

"'No, it's not the Mounties. Rosie, here comes a blind attack. This is what I was telling you about on the way up here. It looks like three men on horseback riding toward us from the northeast mountain section, that forested area up in the mountains. Better get ready for a battle.' Victoria sounded frightened.

"'Hell, Victoria, I was wishing for a glimpse of those good-looking uniforms and maybe what was in them. Surely, I'll have to do their job for them. Are they the police up here?'

"'Yes, they are like the National Police for Canada.'

"'I have them in sight. You just keep going and don't slow up. They are more than two-hundred yards away, and with their six-shooters they are not going to do much more than make noise. I think they are trying to scare us into stopping, but little chance of that; keep your pace up. I can pick them off anytime with this sweet little .30-30 of yours, if they get too close.'

"'I don't want you to hurt anyone, but I don't want us to be hurt either. My team can't keep this pace very much longer. When you want to scare them off, it's fine with me. I admire your shooting skills and maybe they will appreciate them too once you begin to show them.'

"With that encouragement from Victoria, I took aim at the first one. I didn't want to kill them; I knew they were probably looking for money. I aimed at his black hat and squeezed off a round. A second later his hat flew down to the ground, so did his gallop. However, his two friends continued riding toward us at a pretty good pace. 'Guess they can't see I mean business, as my father used to say,' I told Victoria. I pulled off several more rounds, and hit the closest guy in the leg, just below the thigh, maybe the knee. He pulled up, holding his leg. The other one just kept coming even faster than before.

"'Rosie, this rider is getting very close and my team is just about worn out. We've got to do something real soon.'

"'I yelled for Victoria to pull up on the reins, bring them to a halt. When she did, the rider came galloping up very quickly. When he was about thirty yards away, I pulled the trigger. Off the saddle he went, grabbing his left shoulder in agony and pain. 'Don't stop, Victoria, it's nothing but a shoulder injury and he'll live. He won't be happy, but the fall from the horse probably hurt worse than the gunshot wound.' I chuckled to myself, and thought, *I should get a job with Wells Fargo.*

"Victoria slowed the team down to a slower pace and said, 'Rosie, you would have made a great stagecoach shotgun rider in the old days of the wild West. I don't think Wells Fargo could afford me if I could shoot like you. You know in 1852, Henry Wells and William Fargo founded Wells, Fargo & Company in San Francisco to serve the West. The new company offered banking, buying gold and selling paper bank drafts as good as gold, and a Wells Fargo express, which is a rapid delivery of the gold and anything else valuable. If you want me to, I could really get you a job. My father's brother works for them in

San Francisco as a vice president of money transfer. I bet they need someone up here like you.'

"We both laughed again. I told Victoria, 'I like it better when I have Tom to hide behind if I ever do miss my target. He's a hell of a lot bigger shield than you.'

"Victoria said, 'Yes, I can see where there's an advantage to that arrangement. But have you told Tom that he's a secondary target in a case like that?' And we burst out laughing again.

"'Victoria, I was taught by one of those wild West cowboys that worked in a Wild West Show somewhere around Kansas City before he went to work for the same man my daddy worked for in Kentucky.

"'He told me the story of how he got shot in a barroom gunfight with three desperados that came in to rob the place one night. That was a big mistake for the bad men, but Jake and one of his friends got shot. After that, Jake had to spend two months in a hospital out there to save his leg. Still, to this day, he walks with a limp. He was a heck of a teacher. I remember everything he taught me from the age of twelve.'

"'Were you always good with a gun?'

"'Not really, I could hardly hold the gun up when I first started. It took a lot of practice. The gun felt so heavy, but each week it got lighter and lighter until after about six months I could pull up the .45 from my hoister, and fire off six rounds into the target without any difficulty. Then Jake said I was ready to move to the next stage–the rifle.

"'The .30-30 Winchester took another six months, but after that Jake told me, "Now just don't forget you have to practice, practice and practice some more to keep your skill up to this level, no matter how long you shoot. More than likely when you get married and have a family you will have less time and more responsibility. At least you'll always know how to shoot, it will just be your accuracy that will suffer," Jake said.

"'It is marvelous to see a woman who can handle a rifle and a sidearm like you. I want to be sure to teach my girls.' Then all of a sudden, she shut up and changed the subject.

"'Wait a minute, Victoria, you didn't tell me about your girls. All I've heard about is your father and mother. You have to tell me more about the girls; how old are they? are they in school? Do you have a husband?

"'Oh, alright, I'll tell you the other half of the story. When I finished college, my parents moved out here. I just always moved along with them, for I had no other plans. I was then 21 years of age, had never known a black or brown boy to even talk to. I had only known white boys throughout my education in Scotland, England and Canada.

"'When we moved out here again, there were only white folks except a few darker individuals found to be of Asian descent. I became more and more attracted to a young Asian man from Hokkaido, Japan. We were about the same age. He had been to the University of California where his father went in San Francisco. We would talk at length at his father's store in Minton, a general store for ranchers, farmers and miners. My parents and I went in the store each week to do shopping; he and his father seemed very openly friendly to our family. Maybe it was because we were the only non-whites in the area.

"'Be that as it may, we continued to be friends for nearly a year, trying to talk more at length, until one day he asked me to go with him on a delivery to a nearby farm. When we got to the big spread with a huge sprawling house, he went right in without knocking or calling out the owner's name. Then I became suspicious, and asked him to whom the place belonged. He said it was his father's.

"'It was then he told me about the horrible death of his mother that drove his father away from San Francisco. He broke down in tears, and I put my arms around him to console him. Little did I know that was all it takes to set a man off. He didn't waste any time in seducing me into the next step of a love affair.

"'We concealed our love affair from his father and mine for several months but then I noticed my physical condition and how I had changed. We then went to his father and told him of our love for each other. He was happy, wished us good fortune and much happiness. Then we had to face my father and mother. My mother was beginning to get frail and weak from all the moving and hard work my father had put her under over the past ten years.

"'She was extremely happy about our love and wanted to know every detail. Yet, my father was not so happy. He was afraid if I got married and left home it would kill my mother but, come to find out, it was my father who was aging rapidly and feeling every year. I didn't realize my father was more than fifteen years older than my mother. Anyway, once my father told me how he felt, I told Norboyuki.

"""After we are married," Norboyuki said, "I'll ask my father if we can't have a hundred acres of his five-hundred-acre parcel. When he does let us have it, and I'm sure he will, I'll then bring your mother and father over to live with us, so they will be close, and we can keep an eye on them." That has been the way it has been for the last few years.'

"'Wow, that is great!' I exclaimed. 'Can I meet them?'

"'I am married to an Asian man and his name is Norboyuki. He's originally from Japan, not China as everyone thinks, and he is very good to me. He even sent me to medical school for animals in Vancouver. Don't ask me how I decided on animal medicine because there were very few practices for animals at the time, especially in Canada. I had a college degree in languages. I spoke Scottish, German, French and English but never knew what I was going to do with the degree.'

"'Good Lord, Victoria, you have an extraordinary background. I feel ashamed to even complain about any of my upbringing. My family was an ordinary Kentucky Appalachian family. I was the wild rambunctious one in our family. I never even finished high school, I was so headstrong. We lived so far up a hollow, daylight couldn't find us until nearly noon. No, really. My family, especially my sister, took good care of me.

"'We had a great time growing up but had nearly two miles to walk to school, and when snow fell it got pretty cold. Our boots that were leather got wet, and had to be piled around the wood stove at school while we learned our catechisms. But when I look back, it was fun, and I wouldn't change a thing,' I told Victoria.

"'What in the world are catechisms?'

"'It is a series of biblical stories, poems and rhymes to stimulate your thinking, to spur you to remember the alphabet letters, math and fundamentals of whatever we were studying at the time, especially religion.'

"'Well, Rosie, with that, we are seeing the beautiful setting sun, as we are almost home. We did it with just a bit of excitement and gunplay. I'm not sure if we should tell our husbands for fear they would not want us to venture out again anytime soon. I can assure you, however, we will!'"

Chapter 10

The earth has made music for those that listen
Cherokee saying

Poker Talk

Tom had gone into Dawson City to talk to the land office crew about a possible job while he was waiting to supposedly see what the Canadian Railway was going to do about the property purchase. Tom was still putting forth the story he was a consultant with the Canadian Railway but felt he needed to work while there in Dawson City. Tom was going to talk to Erickson about the possibility of working with the land office while he was living in Dawson City.

"This is the gist of what Tom's day was like, according to our dinner conversation that evening, as he told it to me."

"'Hello, Tom, it's good to see you,' came from the front office men upon entering. 'How's your work going, fixing the cabin and getting the fall garden ready? Winter soon follows. The Farmer's Almanac tells us it is going to be a terribly cold winter this year, and that is in accordance with other predictions, like my knees, Harem's shoulders, and Potter over there his whole body aches...' They all laughed. 'Is this your first Canadian winter?' Harem asked.

"Yes, it is. I have been working on the cabin right steady. Think we've got all we can do for now done. Is Erickson here? I wanted to talk to him about a plan I had thought of that would help us both," I said, in a direct and confident manner to Peter. He's the older man in charge when Erickson wasn't there. He's the one we had the brief conversation with when we first went to the office our first day in town.

"'Yes, sir, Tom, he's here in the back office doing some assay work on a few parcels that sold this week. Let me go back and tell him you are here, I'm sure he would like to see you as soon as he can.' Peter left to go to the assay area in the back. He and Erickson returned shortly.

"'Hello, Tom, sorry it took me a few minutes to get up here after Peter told me you were here. We had a big land purchase three or four days ago. The man wanted it surveyed by the end of the week. It is ten acres, and there are only four of us here in the office now. It's hard to send two men out to survey when there's so few of us here.'

"I told him, 'That's one of the reasons I came to see you. I wanted to know if there was a possibility of me working here for you in the land office while I'm deciding on a land purchase myself. I'm familiar with office management, and I'm sure I could learn the assay and survey work if you gave me a month or two at doing it with one of the men."

"Erickson stated, 'Tell you what, Tom. Meet me at the Dry Gulch Saloon this evening. Several guys get together there after work for a drink and friendly game of poker to talk business. Why don't you join us? We gather around four or five in the afternoon and play until eight or nine on working days, and midnight on weekends. We can talk, then that way you'll get to know several of the miners and ranchers around town.'

"I thanked him for the invitation and left the land office to go over to the blacksmith and livery stable where you got the mule and wagon, Rosie, to discuss buying a horse. I like having the wagon but feel like the wagon is too slow if needed to get somewhere faster than the old wagon would carry me.

"I entered the door at the livery stable and bid them a good day; there were two people in there when I came in. In a few minutes the owner came to me. 'Good morning, Mr. Jameson, my name is Tom Smith. My wife, Rosie, stopped in here a few weeks ago and bought a wagon and mule from you, I believe. I just wanted to thank you and see if you could help me out with getting a horse and saddle,' I said, in a friendly sorta way, because he looked a little rough, like he was having a bad day.

"Mr. Jameson's response was, 'Mr. Smith, your wife, Rosie, is a pure charm. She doesn't look a day over fifteen, but she is as self-confident as a twenty-five-year-old schoolteacher. She came in here knowing exactly what she wanted, the price it should be, and there was no way me or anyone else was going to have her pay a cent more. I gave her a good deal on what I had. She seemed pleased. Now, what can I do for you?' he said.

"'Yes, she is pleased. Rosie really needs the wagon when she comes into town to load up with groceries and supplies. I need a good horse and a saddle to ride back and forth between home and town. It's about two miles, a little too far to walk, especially in the winter. I may be working late at the Land Office some days and, if I guess right, it's not a place that has typical set hours. Erickson and I are going to talk over the work terms one evening this week. Do you think you can help me, Mr. Jameson?'

"'Come on out here in back where the corral is located. I have three horses; a local miner has asked for one but he ain't come across with nary a cent yet. I would say that means you have first pick of the three. There,' and he pointed, 'that black one with the white mane and tail is my personal favorite. Of course, you may like either of the chestnut mares instead. The black and white is twenty-five and either of the chestnuts are fifteen. The saddle, bridle and works are another ten, that's a real deal up here.

'Some of these old codgers up here will kill for a horse if it ain't branded. But you see that big SS on his right rump? That is from Mr. Stepenstein's herd. He owns one of the big gold mines a couple of miles north of here. His nephew got into a poker game here last week, lost his horse, saddle, and over one hundred in cash. Big haul for one of the regular poker crew. He brought the horse over here to sell.'

"I said, 'Then, that must be the poker game that Erickson was telling me about this morning.' I told him, 'I didn't know they were playing such high stakes. That's big money when you don't have much to fall back on.

"'Well, nonetheless, Mr. Jameson, I'll take the black and white, saddle, bridle and bit for forty-five, not a penny more,' I told him. 'I have thirty-five now, and I'll pay you the remainder after I see Rosie tonight. We have an agreement on money matters over fifty dollars; this is close enough to discuss.'

"'I hate to keep losing money, but I liked Rosie. It's a deal,' Mr. Jameson said, as we walked back inside."

"That afternoon Tom rode home on a beautiful black and white stud. What he didn't think about until halfway home was where we were going to keep the animals during the winter out of the freezing temperatures that are common in the northern Yukon Territory. This presented a real problem for the young couple. Again, we were baffled about what to do now that Tom made the deal on the horse.

"When Tom got home that evening, I had only been there a short time. Victoria had dropped me off at our cabin as she passed on her way to her house that was only another two miles up the road. We were both tired when we got home from our journey to the badlands. I was out feeding Old Fred just before dark behind the cabin. When I walked around to see who had rode up, it was Tom; he had the biggest grin on his face I had ever seen. Here was this beautiful black and white tied up in front of our cabin.

"'Who's that black and white belong to you have out front?' I asked him.

"'It belongs to me. I decided today I needed a dependable way into town when I went to work. That way Old Fred and the wagon can be used by you during the day for whatever you need,' Tom said.

"'Does that mean you got the job with the land office?' Tom didn't say anything, just went in and started washing his hands and face.

"I started preparing dinner. We were having string beans, pork chops, and red potatoes. At dinner, we talked over the day like we usually did.

"'Well, I'm pretty sure Erickson will hire me in some capacity, but he wants to talk over the terms. He wants to do this tonight or some night this week in town after the office closes.'

"'You know, Tom, these days are getting shorter and colder with every passing minute, it's not like Kentucky or Virginia where we're from. We're in the real North now. We have to think of the animals. They'll be all right another month but after that the water will freeze, then the trouble begins. Our first concern the next few days is building a shelter for them. I would hate to see your new pony freeze to death,' I told him.

"He did nothing but smile his charming smile and said, 'Don't worry, Rosie, everything will be just fine. Rosie, I don't feel like riding back into town this evening. I think I will lie down after dinner and think about what we have to do about taking care of the animals.'

"That evening I sat by the oil lamp and the fireplace. It

was August, yet the evenings had started getting cool enough to have a fire. I started knitting a start of what I thought would be a warm wool sweater for Tom for Christmas. I figured it would take me that long to do because of my lack of experience at knitting, and the difficulty at doing the project. But Momma used to say, 'Nothing beats a try but a failure.' I always thought that meant to give it your all, everything you got, don't give up before you do. I wanted to give myself enough time to do all the 'unknits of the mistakes' to get this done in order to give him the gift this year, not sometime in the future.

"Around nine in the evening, before I went to bed, Tom woke up and nearly jumped out of the bed. He said, 'Rosie, you won't believe what I dreamed during my nap. Remember I told you I was going to think about what we needed to do to take care of the animals for the winter?'

"'Yes Tom, I remember you said that just before you went to lie down on the bed.'

"'This vivid dream came to me sometime after lying down. I was out with Paint and Old Fred, my horse and your mule. That was the name I gave to the black and white on the way home yesterday. I thought of my mother wanting to paint everything in our kitchen at home black and white.

"'Anyway, in this dream we had made a makeshift corral out of small trees. The corral attached to the back of the cabin with a gate in the back of the corral for them. We lined the back of the cabin with bales of hay. There was mud in between each bale up as high as we could reach. I suppose that would be about ten feet for me,' Tom said. 'Somehow, we fashioned a dome over the top of the corral and had a piece of tarp or burlap covering the opening to the hut. That makeshift barn hut kept the animals warm this winter until we decided if we would stay.'

"'Tom, that may keep them dry, but it wouldn't keep them warm when the temperature drops below freezing in midwinter,' I told him.

"'Yes, but I haven't finished yet, it gets better. I ran a pipe from the back of the fireplace and brought water into the pipe. You remember I was an engineer on a steam engine, right? Well, I fashioned a heater for the animals, and us here in the cabin, out of the same methods as the firebox does on the steam engine. The only thing I have to figure out is where to get the materials before winter. It would be awfully cold to work after the ground freezes up here in October, I would think. We can't wait much longer,' Tom said, with a great deal of enthusiasm.

"'Let's go out and look at the back of the cabin to see how much room we actually have. It was a little fuzzy in my dream.' Out the door he went in his nightshirt, then he realized it was dark and came back in disappointed. The next morning, he was up looking and measuring even before he had washed up for breakfast. He was fired up like I hadn't seen in a long time.

"'Tom, you are serious about this, are you not?' I said to him. 'If you are, we can get to work right away on a makeshift corral. In a week, we can have a lot done; more, if we can get the materials you are figuring on. For sure we can get the animals out of the weather. I'll have to leave the fire, steam, all that up to you. After all you are the engineer!'

"'Yes, and this is the type of challenge I was presented with as a student at the University of Virginia. My father went there as well, this is the type of thing he would throw at me when I was a kid. Come on, Rosie, let's get crackin'.'

"We went in the cabin and had some oatmeal for breakfast. He talked the whole time about the project. Tom got dressed in his red flannel underwear under his coveralls because there was a cold north wind blowing that morning. He went out and surveyed off by rough measurement a forty-foot by thirty-foot corral. That would give us enough room for the two animals to have room enough to move around and out of each other's way. We still were not sure how they would get along. That day we chopped down sixteen small saplings, skinned and debarked them.

"The next day Tom went to our neighbor, Mr. Jacobson, and asked him if he would lend us his tractor and a posthole digger in order to build the small corral. He had a wonderful fence a quarter of a mile along the roadway to the west. Tom told him of his engineering idea. After he told Mr. Jacobson of the idea for heat, he offered Tom all the hay he wanted to do the hay and mud barn.

"Mr. Jacobson said the natives up here built a similar structure when he first moved up here. I had helped build one in Kentucky when I was young and studying with the Indians. The only thing different was we didn't have bales of hay then, we just used the hay and mud.

"Mr. Jacobson had the latest farming equipment since he was one of the richest men here in the valley. He was willing to help us get the project done in the next few weeks before winter set in.

"To make a long story short, Mr. Jacobson brought his two sons over one Saturday and the men actually built a small house for the animals like Tom had designed on paper out of the hay and mud. Tom had made a deal with Mr. Jacobson to draw a heating system for his house in return for all the work the men were doing at the cabin. In two weeks, they had the wood-burning fireplace rigged to heat up the hot water in a tank that somehow allowed a small amount of steam into the animals' shed they had made from the hay and mud. The animals had a warmer little shed than most of the miners in the valley that winter.

"When Tom finally got back to Erickson several weeks later, Tom said Erickson was angry that Tom had not met with him before then. Tom explained it was because there was no time to waste if he was going to get a shelter built for the livestock at home. When Erickson understood it was the time factor that was significant for us, not that he didn't care about the job, then Erickson was no longer angry.

"Erickson said, 'Tom, just stay in town tonight and play a little poker, and we'll talk about the work that you had wanted to discuss a few weeks ago.'

"Tom stayed that evening and played poker with the

group until after nine. When he got home, I was still sitting by the fireplace knitting.

"I said, 'Tom, you're a little late tonight. I was beginning to wonder if I was going to have to send out a search party for you.'

"'I know, I know, I am late, but Erickson insisted on talking about the position after we started the poker game. Then he got to winning. That stopped him from talking for fear that bad luck would change his game if he talked. Then I started winning, and I didn't want to be distracted. It went on longer than I had planned. Anyway, here I am,' Tom said, apologetically with slightly slurred speech.

"'It's getting late, let's get ready for bed. I'm tired from canning vegetables Mr. Jacobson's wife brought over this week. I'm trying to get Old Fred used to going into the shelter we built. He is still hesitant to go through the canvas we put up for the door. He'll go through when it's up but if it's down far enough for him to feel on his back he stops for some reason. At least he will go in when he's being led; he wouldn't do that a few days ago.'

"'I'm sure you'll figure out how to have him come in the evening, that's what is important. You're great with the animals. Wish I could handle animals, ride and shoot like you; that alone will keep the most undisciplined animals in line, including the two-legged type,' Tom said, as he pulled off his boots.

"'I don't know about that, Tom. Always try not to stay around trouble if I see it brewing. My father would say,

"There are some things you can't outrun." So, you must avoid the area. In other words, stay away from bad people, places and bad things if you can. Reckon he was right.

"'The first snowfall is due this week; it's only the first of October according to the almanac. That means there will be less we can do outside. The fishing hole on the creek will probably soon freeze over and we won't be able to fish for our dinner anymore. I really enjoy taking our fishing pole back there with a couple of worms and bringing back three or more big bass or trout for our dinner.

"'Remember the day we saw the baby bear and worried the next hour where the momma was located? We'll have to start digging into our stock of meat. We have some moose, deer, beef, and pork salted away. Usually, that would be enough back home but I'm not sure about up here just how much we'll be going to need.

"'I'm guessing and preparing for twice as much, since the winter is much longer up here. I'm glad the builder of this little cabin knew about making a meat cooler or a basement area to store canned and salted foods without going outside to the smokehouse, like many do back home.

"'What several of our neighbors like Victoria have said to me is we will get snowed in for a week at a time, two maybe three times each winter. I'm glad I got that old feather tic and homemade quilt from Mrs. Jacobson last month when she offered them.'

"Then Tom said, 'Oh, don't worry, Rosie. I'll keep you warm this winter. Come on to bed; we have to get up early tomorrow.'"

Chapter 11

Forging onward, ever onward, blessed, honored, pioneer!
Author unknown

Tom Starts Work

A few days later, I had Old Fred going in and out of the shelter with no problem. We never had any trouble with Paint right from the beginning, he was a well-trained horse. Paint and Old Fred got along just fine. They would almost talk to each other in horse language and shake their heads up and down quite often.

"Tom came out of the cabin that morning while I was still feeding the animals. I had collected two rabbits, two laying hens and a rooster from Mrs. Jacobson over the last month or so of their visits to work on our little makeshift barn and corral.

"I was thinking about what other animals I could get, when Tom said, 'Well, I've made my decision. I'm going to take the job and work through the winter when there's not much else to do if you're not a miner. At least that will pay the rent and buy groceries for the month.'

"'That seems reasonable. You need to do something to keep you occupied and pay for that fine-looking stud and his outfits you bought,' I told Tom when he was telling me about getting the job.

115

"This worked out well for the first month. He was up at 5 a.m., ate breakfast, and was at work by 6 a.m. He worked until 5 p.m. and then rode back home after he closed the office. He said the most difficult part of the job was sitting doing the bookwork for the assays. Tom was a meticulous person about anything he was supposed to be in charge of doing. I'm sure if they gave him a job it was done correctly.

"Then, one evening in November, it had snowed nearly a foot that day and Tom wasn't home by dinner. Around 9 p.m. he came stumbling in. 'Damn, it's treacherous on the roads even with a horse. You can hardly get through the snow drifts,' Tom muttered, as he stopped at the front door and pulled off his boots.

"He crossed the room without acknowledgment and fell across the bed. I knew right then he had been drinking heavily because Tom wasn't a drinker normally. It showed on him right away, his speech, mannerism, and the fact he could hardly walk. I didn't say a word, simply rolled him over and left him fully clothed just like he fell, coat and all. I thought about what to do to keep this from being a constant problem.

"The next morning at 5 a.m. when the alarm ringer went off in the windup clock, you would have died laughing. I had been up for more than a half hour, had started the fire in the fireplace and our wood-burning cook stove, with a cup of coffee waiting if he was able to function after such a drunk the night before.

"'Rosie, Rosie, where are you? My eyes won't open, my

mouth is dry, and my bladder is full. I gotta run to the outhouse,' Tom said, as he hauled his carcass across the room to the door. When he opened the door, it was solid white, and he stepped right into a solid wall of snow there at the front door. His big body just fell backward in the floor. I started laughing and couldn't stop. Tom just sat there on the floor, as disgusted with himself as with the situation.

"'Rosie, stop laughing, come over here and help me up. I feel like hell, weak as a kitten and my head is pounding. I need to go to the outhouse, what am I going to do?'

"'Tom, that's called a hangover. That's what happens when you stay out and drink too much. You're not going to get my sympathy, no, not one bit. If we weren't snowed in, I'd kick your butt out, you'd be sleeping with Paint. As it is, it's a good thing I purchased a chamber pot from Miss Ireland at the general store a few weeks ago. It's under the bed. Now get over there and do your business before I have to clean it up from the floor, too.'

"I really didn't know what the term 'cabin fever' was that I heard Victoria use describing winter, until the following week. We had been snowed in all week with probably more than a foot of snow two times that week. Tom even had to tunnel to the livestock to feed them; but what was funny is the animals were nice and warm from Tom's heating rig and contraption he fashioned.

"Tom made an igloo out of snow for fun one day in the front of our cabin. The place was enchanting in a way; very quiet and pretty during the day, but oh so windy and cold after sundown. Tom said several times how lucky he had been he got home before the snowstorm that week. On the eighth day, the sun came out and started melting the snow on the roads. Tom decided to try and work that day for the first time in over a week. I think he was getting cabin fever too."

Final Strike

"We had enjoyed a great Christmas season that year, but I was very homesick, not seeing my folks for the first time ever during the holidays. Tom liked his sweater I made for him and he even gave me a box of chocolates I rarely got except once on my birthday when I was thirteen. I guess he got them at the general store, but I never saw them; they usually only had licorice and horehound penny candy at the counter, two for a penny.

"At the end of January, it had snowed several inches one evening. Tom wasn't home yet and I had prepared a nice dinner. Finally, at eight that evening I ate by oil lamp, alone. This was the final strike; no more am I going to sit alone while he is out with the boys. At 9 p.m. that night, I hitched up Old Fred to the wagon and slowly rode to town in an effort to understand this situation. Was I going to stay quiet or was I going to face Tom and confront his demons, which became my demons through marriage?

"I went by the land office and it was as dark as a dungeon, so I kept going. There seemed to be two bars, and the Gold Dust Hotel Saloon open and music coming from all three. It was as cold as could be, our thermometer read zero when I left home; now, around 10 p.m., it didn't seem to be warming any.

"As I passed the hotel ballroom, it was lively with a showgirl dancing on a small stage with men all up close to get an eye full of those long legs and black stockings all the saloon girls paraded around in most of the time.

"The Dry Gulch, where he said they usually played, was two doors down, and across the street was the Whitehorse Saloon where I saw Paint tied up in front, along with eight or ten other horses.

"It looked like there had been a great deal of activity on Main Street because there were ruts two feet deep everywhere. I tied up Old Fred a few doors down, where there was room at the hitching rail, felt for my sidearm, and pulled my holster a little further forward on my right hip.

"I was going to go in this saloon to see what Tom was up to, and why he was so late tonight. There better be a damn good reason, was the way I felt about then. He had promised me several times, being left all alone on a cold wintery night, wouldn't happen again. Well, here it was again for the third time this month.

"When I first walked through the door, no one turned to look; that was a good sign because I was dressed as a man would. There was a great deal of noise for a modest-sized bar, but this was the main watering hole for miners from Forty Mile, Minto, they even came up from

Whitehorse, the supposed capital of the Territory. For some reason, Dawson City pulled all the activity in the evening.

"I didn't spot Tom at first, he had his back to me, sitting at one of two poker tables. There were six players at each table. Tom's table was the closest to the door of the saloon. I stood and watched and listened for a few minutes.

"There were five men in addition to Tom. I only knew Erickson, who was sitting just to Tom's right. A small-framed, dark-haired, clean-faced man with a tan cowboy hat next to Erickson, on his right. Then there was a big, burly, red-faced, red-haired man with a black stocking hat, and one that had a real miner's look, on his right.

"Across the table from Tom, looking directly at me, was a nice-looking, blonde-haired, blond-bearded, tall, slender man with a black suit, white shirt with a string tie, and black straight-brimmed cowboy hat that I would have said is a professional gambler. He had the Doc Holliday look. Next to him was a jovial old codger with long, gray hair, of 50 or 60 years of age that everyone called Pappy.

"I decided, since I was here at the bar, I would have a drink and see what the Dawson City nightlife was all about. I eased up to the bar and took one of the empty bar stools available toward the end of the bar. There were five or six other drinkers at the bar, but the bartender came over shortly after I sat down.

"'What'd yaw have to drink, mister, whiskey or beer?' It caught me half off guard and I said, 'Makers Mark', because that's what my daddy drank, without thinking.

He looked at me and said, 'You are joshing. That's mighty fine Kentucky Bourbon. We ain't got two men in the entire territory with that good a taste,' he said, with a slight snicker, as if I couldn't have.

"I looked at him without saying a word, pulled back my old railroad coat I had taken from Tom's hat rack, and showed my big pearl-handled pistol, then stared back into his eyes. 'Right away, right away,' he said, and brought a shot glass full of bourbon.

"To this day, I wouldn't have known the bourbon he brought me from Wild Turkey, Makers Mark or Jack Daniel's, a Tennessee whiskey; for that matter, any other whiskey because I didn't drink. But I knew where it came from, and it had been around ever since I was a young girl. I gave him a quarter, as was the cost for a shot posted over the bar. I had brought five dollars I hid in my bra. He said, 'Sorry, sir, that is the finest bourbon in the whole territory; it will be more than a mere two bits.' I reached in my bra, pulled out the five-spot, handed it to him. He brought me back the change with a smile this time.

"I sat there a few minutes, trying to make sense of the game while I sipped on the whiskey. I was about ten or twelve feet away, with several men in the bar between us. There was only two other women in the saloon, and they were there as 'entertainment', if you know what I mean.

"I'm not sure, but I don't think anyone thought I was a woman, probably just a young, underage boy, wanting to live the adult life. That was very common during my day because the educational opportunities that would keep you in school were few and far between. Almost everyone from fifteen to fifty was fighting for jobs and a place to work. It was just at the turn of the century, 1901, and many didn't know where their next meal was coming from.

"Even though I wasn't voting, my father supported William McKinley during his run for president. I don't recollect, but I thought I had heard at the bar that McKinley either was shot or someone tried to shoot him after his re-election. Maybe that was what all the talk was about?

"A man got up from his chair and staggered out the door. I moved to his empty chair with my drink in my hand, just behind Tom, close enough to see the cards in his hand if he raised them up off the table. There were about ten like me, gathered around behind the players.

"Tom had been a pretty wise and shrewd card player throughout his day. He said he had learned from his father's friends as a boy, and he played all the way through college into adulthood. You might say he had been playing cards but wasn't a 'real gambler' most of his life. This was his story to me after the first time we discussed his thirst for the game and whiskey at length when he didn't come home until way after midnight just after Christmas that winter.

"I wasn't sure, because I wasn't there at the beginning of the game, but at the time I came in there were still five of the six men playing in the game. Money was piled in the center of the table. I counted over fifty dollars, a month's pay or more for most of the men. They had been around twice and only one person folded. Now they were starting the next bidding; it went around again to Tom. It would cost him five more dollars to stay in the game.

"Tom put up another five but the man next to Erickson, the dark slender guy, about fifty, with no facial hair, stood quickly and accused a man by the name of Alexander of cheating. Alexander stood, pulled his gun, but before he could aim accurately it went off, and Tom was hit in the arm. He fell to the floor.

"I drew my gun and told the guy to drop his weapon. He looked at me and would not, or I should say did not. I then proceeded to shoot it out of his hand, taking half his hand with the shot.

"I then dropped to the floor to see how Tom was doing. Everybody began to scatter when that happened. Several stayed huddled around but no one was doing anything to help. I would have pulled off my hat, but my hair would surely fall to my shoulders. I began to cry, 'Someone see if you can find a doctor.'

"'What's all this shooting about?' someone with a loud gruff voice said.

"I didn't pay any attention because I was tending to Tom. He had a pretty big wound in his right shoulder, with blood running everywhere. The bartender told a big man to help take Tom's coat off. I then tore off his shirtsleeve to try to tend the wound. It looked bad at first but after I poked and prodded a bit I could feel where it went in and came out. It felt like it had missed the bone but tore the upper arm muscle that men are so proud of when they are showing off their muscles; completely off at the end down toward the elbow… it looked awful.

"No sooner had I got the shirt torn off and I was prodding to get the blood stopped, a big hand grabbed me by the collar and lifted me right off the floor like I was a feather.

"'What're you doing, buddy? You a doctor or something?'

"'I'm his wife,' I said, and took off my hat, with my hair falling past my shoulders. When I did, the whole place went quiet. The big man that had the badge on his chest under his coat who had just pulled me off Tom was the 'Sheriff.'

"I grabbed my hat, put it back on, and my hair was almost to my waist. I always had long black hair, but I kept it up in a bun most of the time to keep it out of my way working. I stood a little above his badge on his chest; he was as big as Erickson.

"'Somebody said you shot Alexander.'

"'Yes, I shot the gun out of the hand of the man that accidently shot my husband but was going to try to kill the other player who accused him of cheating.'

"'Someone go get Doc da Josef out of bed and tell him we've had a shooting down here at the saloon,' the sheriff said. Quickly, a man left.

"'Sheriff, I'm going to take care of my husband until the doctor arrives, he may be another hour. I've dealt with gunshot wounds before,' I said, even though I hadn't. I felt I had to be there with him doing something to help.

"'Yes, Miss, go ahead, let me get over there to Alexander who is crying that his hand is shot off.'

"About that time, Tom was beginning to stir. He had either been knocked out by the gunshot or he hit his head on the floor when he fell from the chair after the gunshot. Either way, he was out about ten or fifteen minutes, maybe more, after the initial scene.

"'Am I alive? It looks like I'm in the arms of an Angel,' Tom said, with a faint smile.

"'Tom, you big moose, if I didn't love you so much, I'd shoot you again. Do you realize how close you came to meet your maker tonight?'

"'Rosie, how did you get here so fast? Did someone go get you?'

"'Never mind that, let's get your shoulder and arm fixed up. Here's the doctor now.'

"'Sí, Señor, I'm Dr. da Josef, the local physician here in town. I'm not a dentist, as Doc Holliday, but many say I look like him. I think I'm better looking, even in my nightshirt and red underwear,' he said with a laugh. 'Let me get this wound fixed up, my dear. If you will just put something under his head, I'll take over.'

"After he started looking at Tom's wound, I noticed the doctor was in his red nightshirt. He looked at Tom first, as the sheriff had directed. He did some cutting and sewing on the wound, right there on the bar room floor, where it was as nasty as could be, with Tom just screaming.

"'You're a lucky man. It missed your brachial artery and didn't shatter the bone. I'll stitch you up better tomorrow if you don't live very far out of town. I'll put a cover over it for tonight, like a wrap to stop the bleeding. You'll be all right with a little tender care from this beautiful lady who seems willing to supply it. Are you a nurse, my dear?' the doctor asked.

"'No, I am a midwife, herbalist and wife to this big moose lying here on the floor. I do help Victoria the Vet from time to time,' I told him.

In a few minutes, the sheriff came back over and said, 'Alexander didn't fare so well. The doctor said he is going to have to go to Whitehorse to a bigger clinic to try to save his hand. You're a hell of a shot to take that gun out of his hand in these tight quarters without hurting anyone else.'

"'Tell you the truth, Sheriff, I was more concerned with my husband. I could see where the fire was coming from; it needed to be ended as quickly as possible; that's why I pulled and shot so quickly. He had eyes for the guy across the table, but his gun got hung or tipped by his holster when he drew; that caused the gun to fire over toward Tom and hit him. I didn't want to take a chance of him getting off a second shot, he had to be stopped. He looked ornery and cantankerous about then.'

"'In my opinion, you did the right thing, and I'm not going to hold you in any harm. If the circuit judge has any further questions, he will get in touch with you when he makes his rounds this month.

"'Erickson said you both live in that little cabin on the edge of town. Now, let's get some guys to help carry Tom out to your buckboard. Erickson said you had a buckboard. We'll tie Tom's horse to the back, and he will follow you home. You will need some help getting him in the cabin. Do you want me to send someone, or I can come by in a few minutes after we get Alexander bandaged up to send to Whitehorse?'

"'Just send me someone that is strong. Tom is like trying to lift a moose. I've had to do it several times these last few months. That's really what I'm doing here. He shouldn't have even been here either.'

"'Miss, don't be too hard on him, at least the men over on this side of the street are just playing cards. It's the other side of the street I have to worry about when the wives come to me.' And the sheriff turned his head like he was shy, talkin' about women of ill repute."

Chapter 12

If you always try your best, then you'll never have to wonder about what you could have done if you had summoned all your thunder. And if your best was not good enough as you had hoped it would be, you still could say,
"I gave it all I had in me that day."
Author Unknown

The Healing Touch

That was it for Tom, as far as work was concerned. The evening poker games were now in the past, three months now confined to a 20x20 cabin for the winter, with only me to look at. If that wasn't punishment enough, he actually at times seemed to enjoy it after the initial shock of almost being killed began to wear off. A few more inches toward the chest and it would have been another story, Dr. da Josef indicated on his visits to see Tom at the cabin several times.

"'Tom has six to eight weeks in the cabin with you at a minimum. He can stir around and take short walks but no work or riding, even in the buckboard I see out there. The shaking and jarring would probably open the wound and start the whole process all over again,' said Dr. da Josef.

"At first it wasn't hard to keep him in bed the first two weeks; the pain alone did that. After the pain let up, he would try to get up to walk outside on the warmer afternoons when it got above freezing. I had to get up, start the fire, cook some breakfast, feed the animals, then come in, wake Tom up and change his bandages every two or three days.

"The bandages were made from strips of bed sheet material. I had to wash the cheesecloth material, the blood, pus and scabs from the wound of the arm, then rewrap with clean, dry bandages. Dr. da Josef stopped by again about a week after the shooting and brought me a sling to put Tom's arm in when he began to move around. That also needed to be washed and dried every two or three days, like the bandages. It was quite a chore for me as well to nurse him back to health.

"'Doctor da Josef, I have some herbs that I use with Dr. Victoria on the animals we worked on together, but I didn't get a chance to resupply most of them before winter hit because we got busy with building our corral for the animals.

"'I have plenty of garlic, comfrey, sage and calendula. However, my stores of goldenrod and yarrow are getting low. I have a good supply of the herbs best to heal the gunshot wound, and tinctures I learned from the Cherokee tribe my mother used. Some were not available up here like aloe, achiote, and echinacea. I have to order them special, months ahead, at the general store. In my opinion, these would speed the recovery of Tom's wound. Do you agree?'

"'Rosie, you don't mind if I take my coat off? Usually

it is cold in most people's homes. Is it just that this cabin is small? It's got to be something else. I don't even see your fireplace flaming,' the doctor said.

"'That heating system is something Tom came up with from his days as a locomotive engineer. He somehow fashioned a pipe with water through the fireplace to the barn outback for the animals to have steam heat.'

"'Another little pipe brings the water and steam back here in the cabin,' Tom told him, as he sat there fascinated with Tom's elaboration.

"'We are going to have to talk about a system for my place when you get up and around in a few weeks. I nearly freeze to death in the winter at that building in town,' he told Tom.

"'Rosie, I most certainly do wish I had more like you that understand the medicinal qualities of herbs. We used herbs in Mexico and South America for hundreds of years before this modern medicine began taking over. Pretty soon everyone will forget there was life and health before these prescribed medications.

"'Yes, Rosie, use what you know. Some I know are topical, best used on the wound, and some are teas to be taken internally, like medicine. I don't even know them all like you do; yes, yes, go ahead, and use them to speed up the healing process we are dealing with here.'

"'What part of Mexico are you from?' I asked him.

"'I'm from the Mexico City area, a little village called Cuernavaca. My father was a doctor as well down there for nearly fifty years. He and I could not ever agree on anything, so after medical school I ventured North, and ended in Vancouver because there was less prejudicial bias as I went North.

"'About five years ago, the Gold Bar Mining Company paid me a lot of money to open an office up here. That's how I find myself here in this hellhole! It's funny how people will sell their soul for a little money. But I've grown to love the people here in town now, because I keep meeting fine people like you that aren't prejudiced or have a predilection against people of different types or color,' Dr. da Josef said.

"'That's great; it looks like we are stuck here at least until spring. We might as well make the best of it. I've started on another wool sweater for Tom. Now I think I'll do a sock hat for him next, like I saw one of the men at his poker table wearing. That would be good for Tom to remember the poker game by.'

"Tom spoke up, 'Hell, Rosie, I don't think I'll need anything to remind me to remember that poker game. But I would like to know when I can get up and go into town?'

"'Take my advice, Tom, you were lucky this time. The next incident may be more tragic. Rosie may not be there to back you up. You won't believe how many I've had to give last rites to as I was trying to save their life from a gunshot, stabbing or clubbing in these bars, back roads or just outside a mine. It's like no-man's land up here, no place for decent God-fearing folks like you.'

"With that he smiled at Tom and gave me a hug and said, 'You are so young, you and Tom have so much life ahead of you, please don't waste it up here in this hellhole.'

"As he went out the cabin door, he waved to us and smiled before he got on his buckboard with his black bag. He carried the herbs I had given him, wrapped in a San Francisco newspaper Tom liked to read, with a five-dollar bill I had given him for coming out to see us and helping Tom.

"It was several more weeks before I saw anyone, then one morning there was a knock at the door. Both Tom and I went to answer and there stood Victoria. It was early March but there was still snow on the ground, and bitter cold that clouded, overcast morning.

"'Come in, come in, get out of the cold wind, I haven't seen you in over a month,' I told her.

"'Hello Tom, hello Rosie, I hate to barge in on you two without an invitation.'

"'Hello Victoria, I know you came to see Rosie so just try to ignore me. I'll be over here in the corner reading my paper for the third time this week, but it seems I find something new each time I read it,' Tom said to Victoria, in his most charming voice.

"'Yes, yes, Rosie, I have been busy nursing our family back from a terrible cough and fever. It acted just like whooping cough. I wasn't able to get anyone to verify my diagnosis, just had to go with what I thought. Thank the Lord, I didn't get it too, just my husband, and children. I was afraid it was the bad flu at first, when the coughing persisted for over a week with each of them. Now, thankfully, they are a little better.'

"'That was bad enough, wasn't it, Victoria? I've just about got Tom here fixed to where he is going to be able to help around here some again by dressing and feeding himself. The entire month of February was spent right here in this tiny cabin, except to feed the animals, and we couldn't even do that several days the snow was so deep. We both got what you call cabin fever. We know what that is now for sure.'

"'Rosie, what I wanted your advice and help with is two things. First, some herbs that would help my family get back to feeling decent. Like a tonic or a tea? They seem so weak and have no stamina,' she said wearily.

"'Yes, like a tonic or a tea they should drink two or three times each day. Come over here with me and we'll see what we can conjure up for you to take home with you. It would be best to use something like peppermint or blackberry in the morning, like a breakfast drink, then chamomile in the afternoon. Chamomile is a little hard to get used to as a youngster, but my mother put half a teaspoon of honey in ours each morning. She said that boosted the properties of the tea with the honey by mixing them together. I'm not sure if that's true but it sure made it taste much better. Honey does have a lot of healing qualities itself; I always have a jar or two around. Do you have any, Victoria?' I asked.

"'No, I'm afraid not. I'm sure willing to use it if you

think it will help them take something like the herbal tonic; they are all like the walking dead right now.'

"'Here,' I said, 'I think I have two jars. Take this pint jar with you, along with the peppermint and chamomile tea. When you run out of that, maybe the weather will be good enough you will be able to get some at the general store in Dawson. There has to be someone here that keeps bees and sells it fresh,' I told her.

"I took her over to the table and showed her how to measure out the tea, because a little goes a long way. 'I usually heat up a teakettle with six cups of water in it. I know Tom will drink a cup or two, I will drink a cup or two, then if we want a cup in the evening, we have enough left.'

"'Do you just drink the tea leaves and all?' Victoria asked.

"'No, you don't have to drink the tealeaves. Put a piece of cheesecloth over the mouth of the kettle to strain the tealeaves out when you pour it. Of course, later you will learn there are excellent herbs that come from the root of the plants, like ginseng, that could be used that don't have the leaves, but I haven't seen it up here in the forest anywhere. The climate may be too cold to grow here, I'm not sure. If you are interested, I'm sure we could find a source in San Francisco or some big city like Seattle. Ginseng is used a great deal and is very common in the Appalachian Mountains where I was raised, but I was told by an Indian that it came from China.'

"'Rosie, this is great. This is just what we needed to help

everyone get back on their feet again. You and Tom will have to come for dinner when the weather breaks and we can get together. I better get going now. This is the longest I've been out of the house for a month.

"'You know, we have about five acres of land that is not plowed for anything else now. I think I will talk to my husband about using it for growing herbs. There's a fence line I could use to plant blackberry vines and other vine plants as I learn more about their value to my animal practice and my family,' she said, excited for the first time in months. 'Maybe you can come over and show me some planting tips later, when the ground gets tillable.'

"'Victoria, don't hesitate to let me know if you need anything. We'll try to get it for you if you both can't leave the children. After all that's happened, with all the time Tom and I have had for some good long talks about starting a family, I think that's in our immediate future,' and I gave her a smile with a wink as she went out the door that day.

"'Goodbye, you two,' Victoria said, as she waved from her wagon that morning."

Chapter 13

The best way you can find out if you can trust someone is to trust them.

-Ernest Hemmingway

Good News for Rosie and Tom

It was almost another month before we could get out much, because of the weather. There were a few days it warmed up to 35-40 degrees, but at night it still dropped below freezing. We could get out a few hours at mid-day; after that it would begin with a cold north wind and by nightfall you had to be inside.

"At the end of February, Tom and I would ride into town in the wagon because his shoulder was still painful to move much, buy supplies, then right back home before it rained or snowed.

"On our next trip into town that month, Tom asked if I would mind stopping in to see Erickson, and everyone at the land office. It had been two months since we had seen any of them. Tom was out of the sling but still couldn't use his arm much. After going to the general store to buy our supplies, we went on over to the land office.

"'Hello, everyone,' Tom said, as we walked into the office.

"Eyes turned toward us, then a great round of applause from the four guys in the front. 'There's our survivor and his gun-slinging partner,' they said in unison, with laughs and smiles. Nothing in the office had changed, even the desk looked the same, piled high with papers as well as rolled up plans. Erickson was still in the back, and Rupert his assistant went to get him while Peter talked with us.

"'Look at this! Don't you two look just dapper, all cleaned up, looks like you are going to church. Really, come on back here and let's talk,' Erickson said, in his usual grizzly-bear-like voice when he finally came out.

"He took us back to his private office that had a heavy-armed chair and three smaller, more comfortable leather chairs around a table.

"'This is my conference room. Sometimes we need more privacy than is available out front, with all that's going on out there. Now, tell me Tom, how do you feel? Is your arm well enough to shuffle a deck of cards yet?' he said, with a laugh. 'No, I am really just joshing you. Tell me, Rosie, how's he doing? I wouldn't believe anything he says anymore. He told us he had your permission to play cards that night.'

"'Tom's a lucky man. He's had a private nursemaid for nearly three months, while the rest of the world has had to work like hell to keep going without him. Really, he's doing better now, out of the sling, moving the arm about pretty good. He stopped using the sling last week and now only uses it when there may be a problem carrying something he should not carry like heavy bundles of firewood, bales of hay from the Jacobson's, or something like that.'

"Tom said, 'But it still hurts to do much of anything around the cabin, like washing clothes, dishes, chopping wood, even carrying wood is a real strain!' Tom begins to laugh; even he couldn't keep a straight face with all the stretching of truth that was going on.

"'You've just about milked this long enough, I guess. It's full speed ahead next week, I'll see to that,' I told Tom.

"'Tom, you and Rosie look good. I hate to tell you, Tom, but I had to replace your position this winter. The company finally sent me a permanent replacement. A miner from Ireland who stands about 6'6" and weighs over two-fifty. The company thinks he may be able to replace me for a year or two so I can go back home and see the wife and family. You know it has been over two years now. I was supposed to be able to go back home four weeks every year, but it didn't happen the way everyone back at the main office thought.'

"'That's wonderful, Erickson. We just stopped by to let you know I have decided to change positions, too. Go back to the railroad, something I know is much safer. I operate a one-hundred-ton train more safely than playing a game of poker up here in the Yukon with these outlaws!' Tom and Erickson both begin to laugh.

"Erickson laughed as he shook his head in agreement and said, 'I feel about the same way when I set up to shoot a transit on a piece of land that we're going to survey. I have to watch for bears, mountain lions and most of all outlaws! Rosie, take care of this big moose, as you called him the night we tried to pick him up off the floor in a puddle of blood. Remember that, Tom?'

"'How can I forget it? You guys will never let me live it down.'

"Tom stood and put out his hand to Erickson. The two men shook hands that day in agreement, 'We may never see each other again but it was good to meet good people and have good times, as well as tolerate the bad,' Tom said, with a smile.

"We went back to the general store and picked up the groceries to take home. On the ride home, I asked Tom if he was ready to go back to Kentucky. Tom said, 'The Yukon Territory is abundant with resources that I really like and appreciate. We can walk out our back door, fish, hunt for elk, moose even bear. We can grow a garden, have our animals, and a cute little cabin with the best heating system west of the Mississippi. I'm not sure what it is that we are missing up here, except a nice long summer.'

"'Tom, I'm happy with you. We'll do whatever you think is best,' and I hugged him close.

"Tom said, 'It's damn sure much harder to make a living up here. The work year seems much shorter, that causes you to have to work harder to make up for the briefer time, but the nights seem longer, that's why I would lose track of time when I played poker!' And he laughed, real hard.

"'I think you have learned your lesson,' I told him.

"'It's just all messed up, as far as I'm concerned. Rosie, I am uncertain as to where I want us to land for good, but I think I'm ready to head back East. I'm not sure if the gunshot took the sting out of me or if I'm just ready to admit I'm a little homesick. I know one thing— I'm going to see if there's not a more direct way back East than what we took to get here. Rosie, it sounds like you are ready yourself.'

"We both laughed and cuddled up close on our ride back home. What seemed like such a trudge for Old Fred and me appeared to lighten a great deal that day. As we rolled around the curve, we could see our little cabin in the woods, there in the white frozen forest of the Yukon. I really would miss the cabin, land and the neighbors we had gotten to know. Doc was right—this just was not a good place to start a family."

Surprise, Surprise

"Two weeks later, I was knocking on Victoria's door. I needed to ask her some personal stuff that Tom didn't need to hear until I knew for sure the answer.

"'Good morning, Norboyuki. Is Victoria available?' as he invited me into their home. Being a polite gentleman, he excused himself and said he would find Victoria, that she was there in the house with the kids. In a few minutes she appeared in the foyer of their beautiful home.

"'How is the family doing with their herbs and teas? It's been several weeks now since we talked. I brought you a little resupply of some of the herbs. If the kids don't want to take the chamomile, let's try comfrey, they may like it better.'

"'Come on in, Rosie, don't stand out there in the foyer. The kids are taking the herbs about as well as can be expected. Norboyuki and I forget to take them sometimes when we are in a hurry. Should we take them twice in the evening if we forget in the morning?'

"'No, of course not. We don't want it to be a chore. Just take the tea, especially when you stop during the day to rest. I suggest to many to take a cup of tea halfway between breakfast and lunch, like ten o'clock, and again between lunch and dinner, like three o'clock. If you're not home, like many times, just do it in the morning and evening or either; just don't make it a chore. Don't get all bowed up about it, just have a cup as soon as you can.'

"'Well, Rosie, tell me what else is on your mind. I can tell there's something else you want to say.' Victoria knew there was something more I needed to talk about. I felt almost shy at first.

"'Victoria, I have been having some strange physical feelings. I stopped my monthly from mother nature. I'm usually very regular, you could almost set a clock by it since about twelve years old. Now, all of a sudden, I have stopped.'

"'Rosie, sit down over here at the dining table. Let's have a cup of peppermint tea.' She smiled because she had some already made.

"'I'm amazed at the size of your house. You even have a dining room the size of our cabin.' She then told me, yes, there are four bedrooms upstairs. Then quickly changed the subject back to me. 'Has anything else changed with your health, like sleep, eating, toilet habits, has this ever happened before?'

"'Well, to tell you the truth, I didn't have my monthly last month, and I have been getting a sick feeling when I eat, but it only happens with certain foods at certain times. I can't seem to get a handle on what it is, and I thought you might be able to give me some insight on a condition such as this.'

"'Yes, yes, Rosie, I most certainly can. I think you are of child. Have you noticed any weight gain?'

"'You know, now that you say something, I have noticed my stomach pooching out a little. I thought it was just from not being very active this winter. Victoria, you really think I could be? You know, Tom and I have been talking about going back home and finding a new place to live. With this news, we may have to have a little larger place than we thought.'

"'Yes, I would say you're a little more than two months. If you two plan on going back East to Kentucky, Virginia, or Tennessee to your homeland, you better move up your timetable. You might want to think about selling your place in order to leave here in plenty of time.

"'This will be the fastest nine months you will ever experience…and I might say the happiest! Because, believe me, raising them is a full-time job. I've been lucky my husband is here at the farm to help take care of the kids like a mother hen when I'm not around. Let's hope that Tom is half as good about those things as Norboyuki has been.'

"'Victoria, this is certainly good news to me but I'm not sure how Tom is going to take it. Shall I just blurt it out or should I sorta ease him into the subject, and then let it slip out? I've never been afraid of anything, but this topic frightens me when it comes to Tom and me. We want kids, we just never thought it would happen when we weren't expecting it!'

"'Rosie, both my children were, you might say, unexpected. After you get over the shock when it happens, you realize God actually knows best. You two were cuddled up there in that cabin for two or more months this winter; not all that time was used for nursing him back from that gunshot injury, I'm sure. It was just natural that one thing would lead to another and love would blossom during that tender period,' Victoria assured her.

"'Yes, Victoria, that's just what happened. There were plenty of nights that we would fall asleep in each other's arms by the fireplace. We never thought about the consequences, even though we both know about what our mothers taught us about the birds and the bees.' I laughed with Victoria, gave her a big hug, and thanked her for the shoulder of support during one of my weak moments.

"'Oh, your tea was wonderful. I think you have mastered the tea-making procedure. Now, if you can gently push the children into at least a cup a day, they will benefit as well.'

"That evening at dinner, I brought up the subject of children, our future plans, and if we were thinking seriously of going home in the spring. I worked the conversation around to the fact that I wanted to be with child, and would he want it as well. Tom seemed elated to talk about the possibility. He couldn't wait to say something.

"'Rosie, I can't wait until you are with child. It would make me the happiest man in all of the Yukon. You want to start on the job after dinner?' Tom said, with a charming smile.

"'You don't have to worry, Tom, you already have a head start on the subject. Victoria thinks about two months.'

"'Rosie, really! I can't believe it. That's wonderful! I can't wait to tell the whole town.'"

Chapter 14

Wagon ruts reminder of our past tracks, freedom seekers journeying to a new land.

Author unknown

Homeward Bound

It was the end of March before we could even think of doing much outside, due to the snow and the cold north wind that seemed to never let up. Then one morning, on March 25, 1902, the sun came out like it was summer.

"Tom had been waiting for the weather to clear so he could go to the land office to tell Erickson the good news of us being in the family way. Tom usually wasn't very sentimental, but it seemed like the news of him being a father certainly brought out a new side I had never witnessed.

"Tom saddled and left on Paint shortly after breakfast, with the morning sun warming the trail for him that day. It had been a full nine weeks, and he said his arm was feeling much better. He was able to saddle and mount Paint without any difficulty. A few weeks ago, that caused him a great deal of pain to even try. I knew then he was doing better.

"When he got into town, he said he went straight to the

land office. 'Hello, fellas, you're looking at a new poppa to be!' Tom said, to the whole front office.

"'It wasn't a very cold winter for you it sounds like. No, indeed, the fires were burning at home real hot, weren't they, Tom?' The guys laughed, then Tom agreed with a vigorous headshake.

"'Go on back, Tom; he's just making notations on our last transaction yesterday,' Peter said.

Tom kept walking back toward Erickson's office, just smiling. He knocked on his door and then walked on in, 'Erickson, you won't believe it…I'm going to be a poppa in a few months. Rosie told me last evening I was going to be a poppa. She is about two months along, she thinks. That means the cabin property will not be bought by me, like I thought. Now you don't have to do anything before you leave for home next month.

"'No, I'm serious Erickson. Rosie is about two months along so I want to sell the mule, horse, wagon and all and take the train back to Norfolk, New York, or wherever I can get back East quickest and easiest. Is there a faster way back than the way we came up here that took over a month?'

"'Tom, slow down, take a breath. Women have been having babies a long time and they are stronger than men, if the truth be known. We'll get all that taken care of, but you have to just take one step at a time. First it will take a few days to get you two tickets back to the East from San Francisco, I imagine. Seattle is getting a pretty good rail service up this way but they usually just freight stuff up and down from here to Mexico. I'll check on that. Now, what else you want to unload before leaving?'

"'Yes, Paint, my horse, saddle and all totals about fifty; Rosie's old mule Fred, and her wagon, about fifty for those two; so about a hundred dollars total. Wish it wasn't so wild and dangerous up here, it's just no place to raise a child.'

"'No, Tom, you are right, it's sure no place to raise a child. Actually, we don't even have a school here in Dawson City. Mrs. Buckner, the pastor's wife, teaches the catechisms, plus elementary math and language to the five or six kids of the miners living in the valley. Most men have come up here without their wife, looking for a fast strike; very few are long-time miners. The only women are the harlots and barmaids you'll find up and down the valley from Dawson City to Whitehorse.'

"'How much do you think two tickets are back to the East Coast?' asked Tom.

"'That's something else I'm not sure of. We haven't had many people come up here then go back quite as quickly as you two, or should I say three now, unless it was in a pine box. To get an express, like I believe you're talking about, is going to take some time and money, I'm afraid,' said Erickson.

"'I have about two hundred left; if I can get a hundred for the horse and wagon, that will give me three hundred. If we can then get to San Francisco and get an express train

East for less than that, it would be great. I'll go over to the livery stable and see what kind of deal Mr. Jacobson will work out with me on the livestock and wagon.'

"'Let's sit down here and draw up some legal paperwork to put all this in print. You know, in a few weeks I'll be going back to London and then to my home, too. Hopefully, I'll have your place rented by then, 'cause things turn over right fast in this gold rush.'

"They sat down, Tom and Erickson, and drew up the papers. 'Oh, Erickson, there's one other thing I need to do before we leave. Would you tell me who or where I can get a gold nugget or two from the local mine just north of here? I want to surprise Rosie with a gift.'"

Gold, Gold and Gold

"'Sure, Tom, we can do that today right down the street. Mr. Eaton has an office for the mining operations. I'll go with you in just a few minutes. Let's get these papers drawn up, then we'll head that way.'

"In about thirty minutes, they walked into the offices of Alex McDonald. Mr. McDonald was a businessman who bought claims from men who had either got all they wanted or all they could afford to mine or pan for a claim.

"'According to Joseph Smith at the Register's office, he is buying up everything on the Klondike River, especially the Bonanza Creek and Rabbit Creek areas near where we lived. Talk is he's worth millions from buying and selling these claims. I know he keeps our office awfully busy. Talk is he has gone into business with Miss Mulroney, the owner of the new Fairview Inn. That place will cost you upwards of twenty-five a night to stay there but it's one of the nicest places outside of Seattle and San Francisco to place your head,' exclaimed Erickson.

"'Yes, I think Victoria spoke of Miss Mulroney's good fortune building small cabins like we live in, when she and Rosie were talking one day on their way up in the mountains north of Dawson City, going to treat some animals.'

"'I think he is the director of mining operations for Kinross Gold L.T.D, London, New York, San Francisco, one of the biggest in this area,' Erickson added.

"Erickson introduced us to a very strikingly handsome gentleman, Mr. Russell Eaton. Mr. Eaton had the sobriquet of 'Flash' from his days riding horses. Mr. Eaton was supposed to ride in the Kentucky Derby, but he and another jockey were racing and the other jockey pushed him from his horse. This playful incident caused a severe broken leg and the end of Mr. Eaton's professional career.

"Mr. Eaton talked with us a few minutes, then sent for a big young man, one of McDonald's hired men. 'Freddy, would you take Tom and Rosie here to the main mine shaft and let them see the glories of the mining world? Then down to Bonanza Creek to the latest claims. Let them experience some panning for the gold, so they then can see the different ways we procure gold. They'll like a day or two of that life, I'm sure.

"'Anyway, Fred, they can bring all they mine or pan back here and I'll be good for their claim. You two go with Fred and he will take good care of you for the day. We'll see you back here in the evening with lots of gold!' Mr. Eaton said with a charming smile.

One of the Gold Mine shafts near Dawson City

"We were never so surprised in our life as to see the deplorable conditions the miners and panners lived in while working their claims. I never thought about the conditions they were living in because we came straight to a cabin. Half of these men lived in what we used to call a shanty or a tent. I don't know how they survived the winter in those tents and shanties.

"As bad as the flies, mosquitoes and stench was

around the area from not having any toilet facilities, I could hardly stand to visit for a short time, let alone for months or years working a claim.

"'Damn, I didn't know how right my father was until I actually saw it. Most of these hundreds of men will never see their investment come back to them. I know a few will hit it big, like the guy that had our cabin before us, but the vast majority will never get any money, and most will go home in a pine box or flat broke.' Tom just shook his head as Freddy took us around in the company wagon that day.

"We got out and panned for gold for several hours on Rabbit Creek, one of the former hot spots of the gold rush. A few years ago, there were still some men bringing in nuggets. Tom found a few small fragments and two nuggets the size of a dime, but that was the extent of our gold digging.

"On the way back to Dawson City that evening with Freddy, we asked him where he was from. He said, 'My family came out here from the Maryland-Pennsylvania area about ten years ago when the gold was plentiful in Northern California. My dad and uncle stayed in California and my younger brother and I discovered this new area up here.

"'A few years ago, there were thousands up here making hand-over-fist gold strikes, but life is hard up here in these frozen, windy mountains. Now there's a new spot we are going to chase down toward Nome, on the cold shores of Alaska. I think the Thornton history must be Viking or Norwegian of some type.

"'My brother and I just love the cold, rough life this place provides us. We have met quite a few young men that just struck out from home, looking for adventure in the West and have ended up here as well. There's a number of us in the valley now and we are all eligible, some looking, and some satisfied to drift from place to place. Me, I would like to find someone and just settle down. I'm now twenty-five and feel like I'm ready for a full-time commitment.

"'Yeah, my family has quite a history across America. One of my ancestors bested Frank James—with Jesse James as referee—in a bare-knuckled fight to keep his prized horse, near Lenox, Iowa, during the aftermath of the infamous Northfield Raid, if you have heard of that. Another ancestor was the notorious Dan "Dynamite Dick" Clifton, who won his nickname by blowing himself out the side of a moving train while trying to crack a safe while moving.

"'Also, surrounded by a mounted posse in November 7, 1897, on the Sid Williams farm near Checotah, Oklahoma, he suffered a broken arm and was knocked out of his saddle by the first shot fired, but landed on his feet and outran the lawmen until sundown. He was quite an outlaw until he met his demise in 1899 in a gunfight in Kansas City,' Freddy told us that day.

"In two weeks, we left Dawson City. We spent a few days in San Francisco waiting for the train that came in from Kansas City. While we were there, Tom got us a room at the Palace Hotel, a fancy hotel, certainly for the upper crust."

"We had some mighty finger-lickin' good food while we were there at the Palace Hotel, too."

Saloon at the Palace Hotel

"With 755 guest rooms, the Palace Hotel, also known locally as the Bonanza Inn, was at the time of its construction the largest hotel in the Western United States. At 120 feet in height, the hotel was San Francisco's tallest building at that time. The skylight opened the center of the building and it featured a Grand Court overlooked by seven stories of white columned balconies that served as an elegant carriage entrance where we rode up. Shortly after 1900 this area was converted into a lounge called the 'Palm Court'.

"The hotel featured large redwood-paneled hydraulic elevators, which were known as 'rising rooms'; I was afraid to get on alone.

"Each guest room or suite was equipped with a private bathroom, as well as an electric call button to summon a member of the hotel's staff. All guest rooms could be joined together to create suites, or to make up large apartments for long-term residents, and the parlor of each guest room featured a large bay window overlooking the street below.

"I had never seen a building such as that. Tom, of course, had been to New York City and was much more worldly than I was at that time. I didn't ask how much it cost us because Tom acted as though it was a gift from someone. I suspect he called his father and spilled the beans about our new arrival, and his father told him to find the best place he could for us to stay. Just my take on it at that time."

My Gold Tooth

"The first evening there, we ate dinner in the lavish dining room of the Palace Hotel. I had never before or since had food served to me by two or three waiters dressed in fancy uniforms; it was a treat. I had goose and Tom had a huge Texas steak. We danced in the lounge and saloon and made the best of our evening. Toward the midnight hour, Tom leaned over the table and gave me a big kiss and a little box. 'Here's a gift from the Yukon. I got you one, and me one. Open it.'

"I opened the little box, expecting a ring because that was the type of box it was, but when I opened it I found a solid chunk of gold.

"Tom said, 'That's from the local mine there in Dawson City, run by Mr. Russell Eaton and crew. Erickson and I went to get it just before we left. It was a gift from the land office and Erickson for the friendship we gained the few months we were there working with them and the town. I thought that would be something to remember this trip by.'

"The second day in San Francisco, Tom took me in a horse-drawn carriage to a street with Chinese people all over. I later found out it was called Chinatown. But anyway, there was an office in this building where it said, 'Dentistry Oral Work.' I asked Tom what the hell we were doing there, neither of us ever had any teeth problems that I knew about.

"Tom said, 'I had this idea that we could both have a gold tooth put in from the gold nugget we have. That way, we never will lose it and we will always have something to talk about when people see it.'

"'I can't believe you are saying this, Tom Smith, Mr. conservative engineer. You actually want to have a gold tooth put in.'

"'Well, I read in the San Francisco paper last night that it is very fashionable now for those people that have discovered gold to hide it by wearing it in their mouth. I thought we could get a tooth done together, and have matching smiles,' and he laughed.

Depiction of early Dental work on Tom

"That's the story behind this gold tooth I have now. It hurt like hell to get it done, but once started, we had to complete the job. Tom said, 'Let's just say, the sailors there in San Francisco with the tattoos have nothing on us.'

"The train out the next morning was a Southern Pacific Transportation Company non-stop to Kansas City. Then we would change, with a day in Kansas as an unplanned stop for railway delay that Tom said was routine repairs.

"After a wonderful day in Kansas City, we took another train from Kansas City to Washington, D.C., and another train to Norfolk, but we were back East in five days after we left San Francisco. Tom had wired his parents and they were there in Norfolk to pick us up. On the way home, we told them about our good news and they were delighted, but I think they already knew. Tom just couldn't keep that secret."

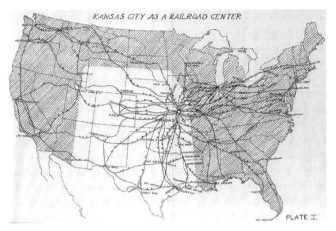

Kansas City Railroad Center

Home Sweet Home

"After we moved home, the next decision was where we wanted to live. Tom decided he wanted to go back to the railroad. There was a small farm in Pikesville, Kentucky, his father told us about, only a few miles from the Norfolk-Western railway line. We rode two of Mr. Smith's horses over to see it.

"On the way over, we just fell in love with the rolling hills; the green pastures and the little house on the property seemed ideal. The owner of the land was in his upper eighties, but his wife had died two years earlier. His children wanted him to move in with them and sell the place.

"Tom and I went to see the man, Mr. Bradshaw. His white hair was long like his beard, eyesight very bad and his hearing was worse. He chewed tobacco and would say a few words then spit. He never knew where he was spitting because most of it ended up on his overall bib. 'Guess that's why they call them Bib Overalls,' I told Tom.

"We only talked to Mr. Bradshaw for an hour or two, then he just came right out and said, 'You young folks seem like you would take good care of my place here. I know my wife would like someone that would take as good a care of it as she did. She worked from five in the morning until five in the evening every day. She raised our six children and they all turned out to be fine young folks like you. If you'll promise to take good care of this place, young lady, like me and my wife, the place is yours for whatever is a fair price.'

"He spit for the last time, got up from his rocking chair there on the porch and said, 'I'm going inside to take a nap.'

"That's how we ended up in Pikesville in 1902. I remember it was such a nice summer there on the little farm we had purchased. The fields were bright green, wildflowers bloomed, and the smell was wonderful. I couldn't believe the difference in being back home after just one year away in the cold Northwest.

"My condition was getting bigger, causing me to have to rest each day a few hours. I finished Tom's first dark green sweater while in the Yukon; it was a heavy button sweater. I had seen a sweater in the Sears-Roebuck catalog I wanted to copy that was only a pullover, with no buttons. I thought a small white diamond pattern would be nice in this new blue sweater I started while I was with child.

"One day, a man knocks on the door about five or six in the evening. Tom had just gotten home from work and we were getting ready for dinner.

"'Excuse me, sir,' he said to Tom. 'I am Mr. Thomas Arnold from the First National Bank of Kentucky. I need to talk to you about the land transaction you recently did in the purchase of this property. May I come in?'

"'Yes, yes, come in,' Tom said.

"Mr. Arnold sat there in our living room and explained to us how we purchased a piece of land that wasn't the owner's to sell. The old man had squatted the land, more than seventy-five years ago, actually took and fenced off five acres that wasn't his.

"'Anyway, the children of the man knew nothing of the indiscretion of their father and are not willing to give up the main piece of land where they have lived for twenty-five years. Your other neighbor who the land actually belongs to, doesn't want to sell. As a result, we have to serve you with this notice. You have thirty days to move,' he said apologetically, and handed us a piece of paper stating the same.

"This is when most people would worry, but worry to me is like a rockin' chair ... you go back and forth but it never gets you anywhere."

Chapter 15

Where the roads are winding and bare, the mountains
surround me, and the people care.

-Rosie 1918

A New Life in West Virginia

We didn't waste any time in going to Welch to find a house close to a railway station. This time we didn't try to buy the place, only rent, since we were unfamiliar with the town and the people at first. Tom knew a few of the railway people but that was about all. The town was lively. The railway went straight through the town with a nice big station where Tom kept his engine each night.

'One thing that happened about this time, I remember, was Tom bought one of the first Ford automobiles in Welch.

"Tom said, 'I don't have the time or the location now to have horses, wagon and animals. Instead, I want to get one of these new automobiles Henry Ford has come up with. The production just started this year, it's called a Model A. Rosie, I think I'll get one to take you to the hospital when it's time. That way we can be sure to be there on time and carry a bag with us at the same time.' He just smiled, knowing this would soften me up to his

163

major purchase of the automobile.

An Illustration of the Ford Automobile

"Sure enough, he took me to a new place in Welch that sold automobiles and asked me what color I liked best. Of course, I selected a blue one, since I didn't care for the black, green or beige autos on display. Tom drove around Welch, proud as a peacock in his new Model A that year. We kept it until after the First World War, I believe.

"I wrote Victoria three letters before I received one in return. In her letter, she stated:

Dear Rosie,

We have had a very trying year so far. I finally got a diagnosis from a San Francisco hospital. The family had a very serious strain of the flu, brought in from somewhere, they called the avian flu. That means it was caught from a bird somehow. Sure enough, after talking to our youngest son, he admitted he had found a dead bird and took and buried it but had forgotten to tell us about it. The doctor here thinks the whole family got it that way. Shortly after your departure, there was still some snow on the ground. Norboyuki slipped getting off the wagon and broke his wrist trying to catch himself from the fall. But for the Grace of God, I have been doing as well as can be expected. I'm now nearly thirty and beginning to feel my age, as age has a way of leaving you something to carry with you, regardless be it physical, mental or emotional each year. That's what my mother called life's burden. Now I know what she means!

You take care of yourself. I know you are going to have a healthy, happy baby. I'll write again as soon as I get everyone healthy on this side of the country. Oh, we planted almost an acre of herbs in the field I told you about.

Your friend, Victoria

"Tom liked working again for the Norfolk-Western Railway out of Norfolk, Virginia. He caught his engine each day at the Welch station. He would either go into Grundy, Virginia, Bluefield, Virginia, Gary, West Virginia, Bristol, Tennessee or back to the main terminal in Norfolk for a delivery, meeting or maintenance. He was always back by five in the evening, except for one time his engine had to stay overnight for some repairs, as well as the regular maintenance in Norfolk.

"He went to see his supervisor about the changes in the schedule and stops that were being made. He was told that part of the reason was there were several highly experienced engineers pulled into the military for duty for their country and Tom had to take one's place out of the Welch station. The supervisor wanted Tom to move into his position in Welch. We made arrangements to be in Welch permanently.

"I began to have contractions and was taken to the hospital in Welch, where I gave birth to a son in January 1903. We later named him Hillard Thomas Smith. This time we moved to Hemphill, a small town outside of Welch, West Virginia, in McDowell County. Hemphill was the largest coal-mining town in the entire state and McDowell County would later become the largest coal-producing county in the United States.

"Tom continued on with the railroad, and I continued to raise Hillard until the uprising in Europe that brought on the First World War in 1914. Things got very tight for most around that time, due to the war efforts of the United States, as much as President Thomas Woodrow Wilson tried to remain neutral.

"When Hillard was about fourteen, he came home from school one day and said, 'I'm going to join the Army to help win the War. The United States needs young men, I read in the newspaper this morning at school. Several of my friends are going to give the wrong date of birth on their enlistment papers. The recruiters aren't blinking an eye with fourteen-year-olds joining now. They are calling them Doughboys; by the time we would be finished with our training, we would be a year older and can rise to the task,' he said, very manlike.

"I listened to his teenage boasting. He was much like his father, over six feet at the age of fourteen, but I grabbed him by the ear, pulled him down to me, and told him in a gentle but very firm voice, 'Hillard, forget about trying to join the Army or any other branch of service. You are going to finish high school. After that, if you decide you want to go to the Army, we can have this discussion again.'

"I let go of his ear, he went to his room for the rest of the evening, but he got up the next day and went to school. I never heard another word about going to the Army after that day.

"Our whole family stayed safe and relatively financially stable because the miners were busy providing coal for industry and war effort. Women in the First World War were mobilized in unprecedented numbers on all fronts. The vast majority of these women were drafted into the civilian work force to replace conscripted men or work in greatly expanded munitions factories. Thousands served in the military in support roles, as nurses, clerks, assistants in military duties like police (M.P.s); even in Russia and a few other places, some saw combat as well. I was a mother, so the need never arose for me to serve."

The Spanish Flu

At the end of 1917, there was an alarming number of influenza cases in Welch. The situation grew grave very quickly.

"'The Spanish influenza is reaching an alarming stage here; thirty-eight cases were reported yesterday,' Tom's boss wrote in a memo to the engineers.

"Oct. 11, 1918: 'Five died last night of the men who left Carnegie with me, two are in the hospital now,' he wrote.

"Over time, Mr. Scott Nelson, Tom's boss, detailed his son being moved from the barracks at the base he was sent to for Army training into smaller tents with fewer soldiers. While the staff got the illness under control, the quarantine took its toll.

"'Yesterday was a most beautiful day,' Scott wrote on Oct. 14, 1918. 'I would have loved to get out and see the surrounding towns and country, but the quarantine has not yet been lifted. We have to content ourselves with pacing to and fro behind the iron fence that encircles the camp, caged in like a lot of animals at the zoo...'

"Several of our friends went on to discuss their vaccinations they received. 'They speak of their first and second shot,' Tom said, 'Well, I got mine and believe me I was some kinda sick for several days. In fact, I was so sick that one of the assistant engineers had to put me in bed at the Bluefield station, take my run and pick me up in the afternoon when he returned; then I still didn't feel well. But today I am feeling in first-class shape again,' Tom said to a group of men, as he went back to work.

"The 1918 Flu Pandemic claimed more than 50 million people worldwide, including 650,000 in the United States. Mr. Scott's son survived, married and became a lawyer.

"This brief window into my friend Scott and his son's life is both historical and personal for me. I can picture Momma fighting the flu in the middle of the war in 1918,"

Rosie said. "I see a lot of similarities.

"I did continue with raising a family. During the war, in 1915, our daughter Josephine was born. In 1919, William Howard was born; then my final contribution to the world population was Nora Mae on December 16, 1921.

"After the fourth one, Tom and I decided we needed a break. We had survived a Gold Rush, World War, Spanish Flu, and four kids. What else could a couple ask for? We concentrated on raising the kids.

"Hillard was now a man and was no longer living at home. He went on to join the Civilian Conservation Corps (CCC). Little did I know there were a lot more life intrusions for the future. I will have to say that probably William 'Rink' was the most rough and unruly child of all of my brood.

"The next daughter, Leona, was the very best a mother could ask for in terms of a good disciplined child. Leona worked around the house until it was school time, then she walked to the school every day until graduation. She fell in love with a boy by the name of Shirley Gibson her senior year, she graduated, and they got married.

"But Rink was my star child; he was tall, dark and handsome like his dad. Rink went on to become a Master Sergeant with three stripes up, three down, with a diamond in the middle. I was told that was as high as you could go in WWII as an enlisted man. He also went on to serve in the Korean War as well. Rink had a very distinguished career in the Army. He was a tank commander during the war and a Military Police commander after the Korean War.

"In the winter of 1932, Tom and an assistant engineer were backing a steam engine into the docking area when Tom's foot slipped when climbing the ladder into the engine. Tom ended up under the gigantic wheels on the train track and was killed instantly before the other engineer could get the train stopped. Services were held in Welch."

Tom was a really good man, she said repeatedly that day.

"Nora Mae, my final offspring, went on through school as a dark, curly haired beauty. She and Rink went through school together and were very close. Nora made the guys swoon for her, but in 1935 she fell for a musician and coal miner by the name of John Fleming Stump, and in 1937 they were married.

"My other children, Hillard, Leona, and Rink were adults and on their own. Hillard and Leona had gotten married and Rink was deciding if he wanted to join the Army. I kept waiting for Nora to tell me any time that she was getting married but that never happened right away, like most.

Finally, Rink left for the Army, and Nora and Flem were happy playing music throughout West Virginia, Virginia, and Kentucky. A few years later they tied the knot. Rink went on and got married in England during the war to a wonderful girl by the name of Elsie Healy.

"In 1946, I got a call from Nora. She said, 'Guess what?

I've got a baby.' She went on to tell me the story of adopting a baby that had been left on the doorstep, you might say, by the father, Curtis Draper. (See story notation at end of chapter.)

"Yes, 1946 was declared the year of the baby boomers. Charles DeGaulle, the leader of the French government, steps down after the war. More importantly, my old friend Nellie Bly got a play named after her at Adelphi Theater in New York City.

"You know, Tom went to watch Jackie Robinson, Hank Aaron and other negro men play baseball for several years here in Welch. He loved baseball, regardless who played. I loved going to the picture show and theater with Tom seeing Lana Turner, Ethel Merman, Irving Berlin and others perform but I went to a few games with him also."

***(For that story read: *One Wild and Precious Life* Amazon.com/Kindle.com 2017)

Chapter 16

Until we meet again
Those special memories of you will always bring a smile. If only I could have you back if only for a little while. Then we could sit and talk like we used to do.
You always meant so very much and always will too, the fact that you're no longer here will always cause me pain.
But you're forever in my heart until we meet again.

Ancestry

During our talks, Grandma Rosie would often bring up how people were related and why. This was because of several reasons, she said. "First, because when I talk it conjures up memories; second, I have to tell it at the time, so I won't forget." Today was one of those days. She wanted to stop and talk about how and why we were related; as a result, she launched into a discourse of family relationships.

The Runyon/Stump/Smith Connection

"The connection of the families was told by John Ben Stump the day your father, John Flem Stump, took my daughter Nora, plus you, Johnny, and me (Rosie) up to see Flem's father in Stumptown, West Virginia. At the time, Mr. Ben was the elder Stump, in his 80s, and I was a mere sixty. After lunch, we all sat around the living room

173

talking about family get-togethers and reunions."

Grandma Rosie cleared her throat. "I will try to remember what Mr. Ben said."

"'The Stumps are an old Virginia, West Virginia family. The Stump roots go back to Pennsylvania, and even further back, you will find the original family came over to America in the early 1600s to New York harbor. The name at that time was Von Stumpfh from North Germany, somewhere near Rostock – Mecklenburg area. Immediately, the immigration authority chopped the Von Stumpfh name to Stump.' Everyone laughed at Mr. Ben's effort to make a joke."

Grandma Rosie said, "I wasn't so much interested in that much family history, I told Grandpa Stump at another time. What I do remember being told most by Grandpa John Ben Stump, when he was about eighty-two years old, while we were having dinner at Flem and Nora's house in Welch one Sunday, was the Stumps were well 'rooted' in West Virginia history, and he went right on talking. I thought that was funny because he didn't realize what he had said was funny!

"'West Virginia became a state following the Wheeling Convention of 1861, at the start of the American Civil War. Our family (the Stumps) was split on West Virginia fighting in the war or becoming a separate state. My uncle Henry Stump was prominent in the Wheeling Convention.

Dapper young Henry Runyon (1902)?

"'Delegates from the Unionist counties of northwestern Virginia decided to break away from Virginia, which also included secessionist counties in the new state. West Virginia was admitted to the Union on June 20, 1863, and was a key border state during the war. It was the only state to form by separating from a Confederate state, the first to separate from any state since Maine separated from Massachusetts, and was one of two

175

states (along with Nevada) admitted to the Union during the American Civil War.

"'While a portion of our family and other residents held slaves, most of the people were yeoman farmers. The delegates provided for gradual abolition of slavery in the new state Constitution that most of the family wanted.

"'Residents of the western and northern counties set up a separate government under Francis Pierpont in 1861, which they called the Restored Government, and Henry was instrumental in all this. Most voted to separate from Virginia, and our new state was admitted to the Union in 1863.

"'In 1864, a state constitutional convention drafted a constitution, which was ratified by the legislature without putting it to popular vote. West Virginia abolished slavery by a gradual process and temporarily disenfranchised men who had held Confederate office or fought for the Confederacy.

"'In 1864, Henry Stump was elected as Roane County Representative in the lower house of the legislature. In 1883, Melville Stump from Stumptown, West Virginia, was elected to the House of Delegates. Melville was the son of Jacob Stump, Sr.; in the same year, Taylor Zach Stump represented Calhoun County in the Lower House of Delegates in Charleston. In 1891, Albert Stump was elected to the House of Delegates; he was the son of Rev. John Stump; my cousin and another cousin, William B. Stump from Hampshire County, were both elected in 1899, and again in 1901. You see, Rosie, why I say the Stump family is well rooted in West Virginia.'

"I told Mr. Ben Stump, as everyone called him, that I didn't know the Runyon family history like he did the Stump ancestry. I know my grandfather's name was William Henry Runyon, he was born in 1853, and passed 1911, and my grandmother was Sylvia "Silvy" Deel, born 1855 and passed 1907. My branch of the Runyon family was from northern Virginia and eastern Kentucky. My father was from Buchanan, Virginia. I have two brothers and two sisters, Christopher, William, Pricey, and Sara. I never stuck around home to get to know much more than that about my family history. I wanted to see the world."

Henry Runyon and Sylvia Deel (Date unknown)

"'Why didn't you go into West Virginia politics?' I asked Grandpa Ben. He laughed and said, 'With all those children, and a sawmill to run, it's a wonder I had time for anything other than work to keep food on the table. But I was blessed with a good family of hard workers. They all grew to be pretty good citizens.'

"There is a somewhat interesting story I should pass along at this time; you all may not be aware of it as it has been a long time since it happened.

"My father's father, sometime right after the Civil War and Lincoln's proclamation about freeing the slaves, had an interesting thing happen. My grandfather was running the Stump sawmill he had started right after the Civil War, some say even before.

"Anyway, he had three black men helping him unload a load of giant trees there for debarking and readying for building. Somehow, a chain broke holding the load of trees and the logs rolled over all of them, including my grandfather, killing three out of four. The remaining person was a young black man, eighteen or nineteen, with a family of three. My grandfather and the grandfather of the black family were all killed. They had been with the Stump family mill for a generation or more and now there was no one to care for the remaining black family.

"My grandfather's brother took and adopted the entire family as Stumps. They then became a new branch of the Stump family sometime in the 1800s. The mother and the oldest, who was a grandmother then, still went by her African name of Nebula and continued to work in our mill restaurant until she was over 90 years old.

"If you come across a black Stump in your travels, that is how one branch got its beginning. The man that lived after the accident went on to name a third son 'John

Nebula Stump' after our grandfather.

"We had a good family dinner that day. I found out Mr. Ben's wife was a Texas Cooper (guess where she was from). 'Trixie Texie', as he called her, had died two years earlier, and since then he said he didn't feel much like doing anything alone. That was about the last time I really talked to Grandpa Ben. He went back to Stumptown to the home of another one of his children where he was living at the time. He died at the age of 84 in Stumptown, West Virginia, at his sawmill.

Tom's Unfortunate Accident

"After Tom's accidental death, I stayed with Hillard and Leona for a few years. Then, after Nora and Flem were married for several years, when they lived on McDowell Street in Welch. Flem was still working in the coalmine, Nora was working at Tony Lambert's grocery store on McDowell Street where she could walk to work each morning.

"One day, Nora called from Tony's store and said, 'Mom, there's been an awful accident. I have to leave work to go to Gary Coal Mine to identify bodies, and to see if Flem is among the dead. Kiss Johnny for me. I'll be home when I know more.'

"There had been a slate fall from an explosion, causing a cave-in of the mineshaft at the Gary Coal Mine, I was told on the telephone that evening when Nora had not returned by dinnertime.

"Nora got home about seven thirty and was crying; one

of the coalmine personnel brought her in. She was so upset she could hardly talk. She finally got out that Flem was alive and being taken to one of the hospitals in Welch. They wouldn't give any details of the injury, only that he was alive.

"Later that week, I was told that Mr. Stump had been crushed in the accident and suffered several broken bones, especially the ribcage, arms, and pelvis. He was lucky to be living and will probably never walk again.

"I don't remember the details but for some reason Nora and Flem wanted to move from McDowell Street in Welch to a little farm someone told them was available.

"The following year, Nora, Johnny and Flem moved out to a small farm of about ten acres near Bluefield, Virginia, called Bluewell. I continued to live with them off and on there in Bluewell while Flem was home recouping from the horrible explosion at the mine, and Nora was home taking care of Johnny and nursing Flem back to health. Johnny was a little over two then.

"They talked of what they needed to do. Nora told me, 'After six months, we can't live without working. Flem has to look for another job but not in the coal mining industry. He is now able to walk, use both arms, but he can't lift much, due to the pain from the crushed pelvis.

"'In the past fifteen years, Flem has been working with a couple of men building churches and office buildings in Welch out of stone, and he has become a pretty good stonemason. He believes he can do that if he hires the men to do the heavy lifting, mixing the mortar, and he does the masonry work. We are going to try to get away from this coal mining area.'

Grandma Rosie with three friends in Welch, West Virginia in 1957 I'm the one with the cowboy shirt and the Boy Scout hat.

"After Johnny was three, I didn't live with the Stumps full time. I would come for short visits of three days, remembering Franklin's advice. I would come more to see Johnny and play with him, ride the horses, feed the animals, go for long walks within the fields and mountains; we had a great time.

"One day when I came to see everyone in 1950, Nora told me, 'Well, Flem thinks he has a job. It will mean us moving to New Ellington, South Carolina. He'll be a construction project leader building for DuPont and U.S. Steel Corporation.'"

"I didn't see Johnny for over a year after they moved to South Carolina. When Flem and Nora got settled, as they called it, I then received a letter. Nora wrote me to say they would like for me to come down for the holidays. Of course, I was delighted, and took the Trailways bus to New Ellington. I brought only enough clothes in my suitcase for a short visit.

"During the Christmas holidays, Flem, not Nora, asked

me if I would stay a little longer after the holidays, maybe a month or more. He said if I would stay, he would build a new bedroom onto the house just for me, with my own toilet facilities. I had never had a bedroom with a private bath and toilet and was delighted to accept the offer.

"After Johnny started pre-school, I was lost most of the day, with Flem and Nora both working. I decided to go back to West Virginia for a while to visit. While back in West Virginia, I tried living with Hillard and his family for a month, then Leona and her family for a month. Rink and Elsie was out in Kansas living on a military base. That prevented me from going out there. All the kids had so many things they were doing they didn't need me in the way. I decided to call Sarah, my sister, who was now living in New York on some island, I was told."

Chapter 17

City Life
Big buildings are
cool, big buses,
big subways are too.
The city is big and fun,
the question is,
are you too?

-Rosie 1951

Fast Forward to New York

Chapter 16 can never be complete from my perspective or from my grandmother's. She simply did not want to complete the New York trip story. I could guess or imagine but she would just say, "Let me tell you about..." then she would go into another story. Somewhat like the one I'm going to tell you about now. This New York connection reminds me of the trip I can personally verify.

Grandma Rosie had come to live with us in Henderson, Maryland, when we moved from Dover, Delaware in 1959. Our family had just been uprooted from living in Melbourne, Florida, the year before (1958) due to the transfer of my father from Cape Canaveral to Dover to work at International Latex Corporation making spacesuits. My dad, John Flem Stump, had worked as a structural contractor on the buildings for DuPont Corporation for nearly ten years. Now he was to work for International Latex Corporation, that DuPont had a big part of, was my take of the transfer at that time.

Grandma Rosie said she lived with another one of her children from 1956 to 1959, during our relocation period from Florida to the Delmarva Peninsula. Once we were settled in Henderson, Maryland, after about six months we got a call from Grandma Rosie.

Sure enough, one Saturday morning Dad says, "Johnny, you and Doug come with me to Dover to pick your grandmother up; she's coming in on the bus today." We rode over to Dover from our house in Henderson just across the state line from Delaware, about a twenty-minute ride to Dover.

Grandma Rosie was around seventy-five or more then. She loved to ride the bus. She would tell me, "Since I lost my horse Diablo, I never found a better ride than a Greyhound!" and she would laugh. Doug, Dad and I picked Grandma up at the Greyhound bus station in downtown Dover around lunchtime, because Dad took us all out for lunch.

A few weeks later, school was just two weeks from finished for the year and I hadn't started my summer job yet. Granny says, "Johnny, want to go to New York with me to see your cousins? Your Uncle Jake will be here to take us back up there next week."

I had met all of the Miller-Horton clan, Grandma Rosie's sister Sarah's family in West Virginia, a few years prior at a funeral but didn't remember much about who they really were at that stage of my life. All I remembered was they were cousins from New York.

Uncle Jake, Aunt Sarah's son, was in his early fifties, tall, dark and handsome. He drove down to Henderson to see if he could take Granny back to New York after his quick visit here with the folks. They spent the next day talking and visiting with Mom, Dad, Uncle Rink and Aunt Elsie while I was in school.

After my last day, Uncle Jake loaded up the car the next day to take us to New York in his big, steel-gray, 1959 Buick convertible; it was really shiny and sharp. I remember on the way up Grandma Rosie, who always had long hair and wore it up in a bun ninety-eight percent of the time, after an hour in the convertible she said, "Hell, Jake, I might as well let it all hang loose like they say in Florida," as she let her hair fly in the breeze on the way to the Big Apple. I always wondered afterward how that saying got started?

It was good to see Aunt Sarah; it had been so long. She looked much older, and frailer than she had the last time we saw them at a funeral of a family member in West Virginia or Virginia. I wasn't sure how old she was. She looked more like an Indian than I remembered. I knew there was Indian blood somewhere in the Runyon family; well it sure presented itself in Aunt Sarah and her children.

We had been in New York on Long Island a day or two when Uncle Jake asked his son, my cousin Skipper Miller, who was a year older than me, if we wanted a job to make some summer money. We didn't even ask what it was, we were that anxious to get out doing something. Of course, Skip was a year from driving; that left Skip's mother to the task.

We all loaded up in the new convertible; they still hadn't told Skip or me what it was we were doing. Skip's younger sister rode shotgun, Skip and I were in the backseat. They lived in West Babylon, Long Island. She took us to a telephone building and backed into a loading ramp like a semi uses. They opened the big steel door and all you could see were telephone books stacked to the ceiling of the huge warehouse.

They loaded us up to the gills. When we left, the rear of the car was nearly dragging the ground. Mom, I was told to call her, gave everyone a job. Little sister, Thelma, was given the list with a pencil. She was to read the address off to Mom and she would drive to the address. Skip and I were the runners. We had the responsibility to carry the big, thick, telephone books to the front door. We started at 7:30 a.m. that morning and had until 5:00 p.m. to deliver one thousand books.

I was stunned, shocked and surprised in many ways how people answered their door. We were instructed to knock on the door and ring the doorbell until someone answered. I'll never forget the scene at this big, beautiful brick home when I rang the doorbell.

This woman about forty answers the door. She was a redhead, as beautiful as a movie star. She was standing there in a completely sheer-white see-thru negligee. I had seen a few girls' bodies up to then in my life but none that looked like a Playboy centerfold. This woman looked like a six-foot voluptuous goddess standing there. She said, "Oh, sorry, thought you were my mailman, but you may be even better. Come on in."

I stuttered and said, "No, I would love to but I'm delivering..." and couldn't say any more. She just smiled a Colgate smile and said, "Come back when you have more time, darling," as she closed the door. I staggered back to the car and told in a whispered voice to Skip to write that address down. He laughed and said, "You like working up here where the girls are a little less conservative!"

I must have had four or more that morning that appeared almost the same. Except one was a man. He came to the door completely nude with his manhood hanging out for the entire world to see. I was not impressed with the middle-aged guy with a pooch belly, and long graying hair with a faint beard. He did not say a word, so I didn't either. I only smiled and turned to go next door with the next heavy book.

Skip came back in the afternoon, smiling, to tell me he had seen a first, and for a savvy New Yorker to admit that was something special, I knew.

"Johnny, in that big green and white house over there were three sisters, I guess, because they all looked exactly the same (remember this is 1959). They were all the same height, close to six feet, because I'm about 5'11". They had long blonde hair. They had music blasting with *Poison Ivy* by the Coasters playing out by their pool because they were all dressed in teeny weenie bikinis with only a string holding them on at both top and bottom. All three begged me to come in because they had been in the pool and didn't want to get the books wet.

"I went around the house to the room by the pool. 'Put them there,' they said in unison, and pointed to a table. 'Would you stay and play with us?' they again said in unison. I said, "Unfortunately, we have to keep delivering these books; we only have another hundred and we'll be finished. Sure would like to stay, but duty calls," and I was out the fence gate.

Skip said, a few minutes after he got back in the car, "You know, who would have thought that we would have such good fortune delivering phone books. We get paid to see all these beauties. I know Dad always said, 'Work will bring you good fortune.' I always told him that was from a poor fortune cookie, but the joke is on me because we have seen today that hard work pays off in more ways than one!"

Later, Grandma Rosie told me, she, Jake and Sarah had spent almost the whole day going to Fire Island to watch the homosexuals. Somehow the subject came up in a conversation they were having that day. Jake said, "Yeah, Aunt Rosie, come on, get in my car, you won't believe this. It's only a short ride down Long Island but it's worth every penny."

"We got out there and, sure enough, there were guys walking down the street holding hands. When we got out on the beach, there were lots of male couples lovin' on each other. Sometimes girls together but most of the time it was guys together; black, white, tall short, Asian, Latin, all kinds. There were several threesomes on blankets, kissing and feeling on each other. I had never seen anything like it as long as I had lived.

"I did remember, I told Jake and Sarah, when I was dating George Pendergrass, he was anxious to meet a man that would have a threesome with him and another woman. I told him not to even think about me going there. George dropped the subject. Jake, Sarah and I just laughed.

"We stayed about an hour. Sarah sat on a bench, she didn't feel like walking. Jake and I walked on the beach, looking at the sights, then we decided to head back.

"Jake stopped for a late lunch with the two of us at a very nice Italian restaurant. I can't think of the name right now, but it was something like Emilio's Fine Dining. Of course, I had my favorite, spaghetti and meat balls. Jake and Sarah had lasagna. We sat, talked about old times.

"Aunt Sarah was sure she wouldn't make it much longer, but I said, 'I feel right spunky. I might even find me a rich old man up here to marry.' Sarah said, 'Hell, Rosie, if you're going to wish you might just as well wish for a young stud of about 50 that's rich and well endowed.'"

And they all laughed, she said.

Uncle Jake drove us back to Delmarva later that week. He again spent the night. All the adults sat up with Jake telling him about all that Grandma Rosie did with Aunt Sarah. He didn't know the lucky occurrence Skip and I had, working, delivering the telephone book gig in New York. Not an experience we would easily forget either.

Chapter 18

*Well here I am in Florida; it all seems so bizarre and queer, the
sunshine, palms and flowers here at this time of year.
I think of all you up fighting ice and snow, gee give me sunny
Florida, away from that northern blow.*

Rosie 1958

Rosie Goes to Florida

We had moved to Florida after my father was transferred from the New Ellington, South Carolina, DuPont job site. This was actually before Granny going to New York with me as we talked about in Chapter 16. I just went ahead with that story since we were talking about New York.

We were living in Palm Bay, a village south of Melbourne, Florida, located on the Inner Costal waterway primarily made by the Indian River. Dad was then working at the Cape Canaveral job site, building launching pads, the command center where they directed the launches. This was a very tropical area with beautiful flora and fauna everywhere you looked. After we were there a little more than a year, I remember one morning my mother said,

"Be sure you come straight home right after school because you have a very special guest coming to see you."

191

After she told me that, I wouldn't leave her alone until she told me who it was that was coming. "Your Grandmother is coming to see us and stay for a while."

I told Mom how happy that made me because she was probably my favorite person outside of my immediate family in the whole world. Mom said, "Yes, she is pretty special to the whole family.

"Try to be at your best behavior because she is getting up there in age now and can't get around like she used to when you both were together in South Carolina and West Virginia." Mom emphasized and cautioned me that Granny was getting old and couldn't do the things like she used to do with me.

"Okay, Mom." Then I left for school just as happy as a lark in sunshine. I was in the eighth grade at Southwest Junior High School. Next year, I would play football for the big Melbourne High School team.

I had just suffered a very traumatic event in my life and was acting out in school in a rebellious way, fighting with the guys in school and being unruly and defiant in the classroom. Almost every day it wouldn't take much to set me off. But when I got home that day it all seemed to lift off my shoulders when I saw Granny.

"Wow, Granny! Am I glad to see you! Are you here for a visit or are you going to be staying for a while?" I asked.

"I'm just not sure yet. I don't know if your mother and father have enough money to pay me to watch you and your brother. Both your mom and your dad say that you have become a handful, and Doug is a very needy child yet," Grandma Rosie said, in a half-joking way and a smile on her face that showed her gold tooth.

"Aww, come on, Granny, I'm your best sidekick ever, you told me. We've hunted, trapped, chopped wood, fished, gardened, and you taught me the flowers, herbs for medical needs, that the Indians taught you. What better partner could you find? Oh, that reminds me, Grandma ..."

With that statement I quit talking for a short time; I was getting choked up. I looked up at my mother and brother with a very solemn face, my mother later told me.

"I was rabbit hunting with two friends a few weeks ago. While we were crossing over an old barbed wire fence, an accident happened. While passing the guns through the fence, the trigger of one of the guns got caught on the barbed wire, went off, and shot my friend. We carried him as far and as fast as we could from the hunting spot, but he still died sometime, somewhere, as we were carrying him."

With that, I began to break down and cry, as I tried to finish the story.

Mom finished telling the story about the horrible accident, and about Harry and I carrying Little Richard nearly a mile out of the woods, trying to get help. "That vision has been difficult for him to get over," Mom told Granny.

Also, she told Granny, "That was one of the reasons

why Flem wanted to take the job with DuPont. To get out of the West Virginia area in order for Johnny to get the vision of Curtis out of his mind, because the funeral was the last thing he remembers that happened in Welch before we left."

"I'm going to lie here a few minutes to try to get the vision out of my mind of Harry and I carrying Little Richard out of the thicket we were hunting that day; we were covered with blood and sweat, it was awful. We just left our guns at the fence. Harry nor I ever could go back for them."

Around 4:30 that afternoon, I woke up to Doug playing the radio to a Fats Domino tune we both liked. Doug had to play the radio and record player only in our room because Mom and Dad didn't like the new rock 'n roll that was in style those days. Doug was just beginning to learn how to play the guitar that we kept in our room.

I went out to the living room where Mom and Granny were talking. I reached in the Frigidaire for the cold water. Granny then said, "You look like you need an ice cream cone."

"I know I'm sure I embarrassed you, crying and having to go to my room. Would you like to get an ice cream and talk like we used to?"
"Is there a place close by we could walk to get one?" Granny asked.

"Sure, Granny, there's Mr. Sullivan's store where Mom works, but there's only a few flavors. The best selection is in Palm Bay at the Ice Cream Shop; they have a great selection. It's really not that far to walk, about 15 or 20 minutes."

"Can I go, too?" Doug asked.

"Sorry, Douggie, you're not quite old enough to tag along with your brother yet," Mom said.

"Well, let me get my bonnet, and walking stick and I'll be ready."

Granny always carried a walking stick after a wild horse she was breaking threw her, and it hurt her right leg pretty bad, she told us back in West Virginia a few years ago. As we walked out the door, she grabbed something off the dresser of the bedroom where she was staying. I couldn't tell what it was, but it was small, and she put it in her apron pocket she was wearing.

Walking through Jungle Park where we lived was the shortest way. Granny pulled out a small knife, and a square chunk of what looked like a candy bar. I thought we were going to share a Hershey Bar or Milky Way because the chunk looked like that.

"What's that, Granny?" I asked her.

"It's chewing tobacco, a bad habit I picked up on the road with my second husband. It's not as bad as smoking tobacco but is a nasty habit. I started to try to keep him from hanging on me all the time. Then I discovered it kept me from getting hungry, plus I could sit in the woods hunting, spit all the empty minutes away," and she laughed. "Johnny, it was something I shouldn't have

195

started, let's put it that way."

"Let me see," I said. I held it in my hand, looked at the slab of Apple Chewing Tobacco as labeled, then smelled it. "Granny, that smells awful. How do you stand to chew it?"

Granny started laughing. "You don't hold back your feeling, do you? Oh well, I'm a grandmother thirteen times over and Hillard made me great-grandmother. I don't have much else to stimulate me these days, now that I'm nearly seventy-five.

"I'm not hung up on it or addicted like many people, because I can stop for days, weeks or months if I have to. Rink won't let me chew at all around his children; Nellie doesn't like it around hers either. I don't do it at all around people that don't like it or ask me not to. I don't do it around children, anyway, but you're not what I would call a child anymore. You're a teenager, almost fourteen now, right? In some countries, you may be married and out working to support a family."

"Granny, I don't want to think about that now. I'm in school to study, and play football, baseball, plus other sports and graduate. Mom wants me to be sure I graduate." Then I thought how nice it was to have her back with us; she was funny, understanding, and kind, but yet firm on doing things the right way.

As we walked along the sandy path going through Jungle Park, there were no concrete paths or sidewalks to follow. I told Granny about what Mr. Sullivan told Harry, Little Richard and I about the park having local snakes, gators, and other wildlife coming out around this time of the year, sunning themself along this path.

"Mr. Sullivan said that a few places here in the development have monkeys in the trees but he admitted he feeds them now, but never had to feed them when he started this place in the early 1900s. Granny, he is older than you and still manages this thirty-acre development."

"I'm not much afraid of any wildlife. I've found that man is the worst beast there is in this world. If you leave most animals alone, they will leave you alone unless they are hungry. Then you have to convince them not to have you for dinner," and she laughed.

"Granny, can you drive a car? I'm getting close to fourteen, and in Florida you can get your learner's permit, and drive with an adult during the day at fourteen. It would be nice if we could drive around together. There is lots to show you, but I go everywhere on my bicycle with my friends."

"Johnny, that's a good question. I would say driving is the same whether it is a mule, horse, ox, wagon or tractor. When I was coming up, there was no need for a driver's license. Sometime after World War I, each state started having driving regulations and laws.

"However, you know Virginia, West Virginia, Kentucky, Tennessee, they didn't enforce regulations, even laws, back in the hollers of our mountain states until much later. Even then, only in the big cities like Richmond, Charleston, Nashville and Louisville, were driving permits enforced.

"Speaking of Nashville, you have a famous Stump relative there by the name of Fredrick Stump, who has a big hotel, restaurant and bar there. I've never been there, but your daddy played music there many years ago. Even my first husband, Tom, stayed there when he was driving the locomotive engine down toward Nashville. He had a few runs to Louisville, Nashville and down toward New Orleans. I never got to go on any of those trips with him; I only went on day trips."

"Granny, a train is a great adventure and being an engineer would be even better. But they don't have steam engines anymore. They are smelly diesel now. Then, Granny, can you drive a car?" I asked her again.

"Oh, getting back to your question about driving. I turned 70 and never drove a car, except one time back in 1927 or 1928, when Tom, the father of my children, my first husband, got bad sick that winter with some flu. It had snowed so deep we couldn't get the animals out of the barn to hitch them up. I tried to drive him to town in his Model T Ford, and just about ran us over the mountain side getting us there. I didn't have any trouble steering, but the gears! The car stayed in the same gear the entire twenty miles. Everyone laughed, but no one had ever showed me how to shift the gears." She laughed at herself. "I was so embarrassed, I never tried to drive again!" she exclaimed.

I laughed, too, with Granny. Then she spit a long stream of tobacco juice over toward a bush and started laughing even more. I hadn't laughed like that since little Richard's death. Boy, it felt good to have Granny back in my life.

We had just crossed an old wooden bridge that meant we were only about ten or twelve minutes from being in downtown Palm Bay. This was an area not driven on very much because it was unpaved, just gravel and stones on the dusty, sandy road. There were a great many orange trees I was pointing out to Granny when an old black Ford stopped, backed up toward us.

A passenger in the backseat rolled down his window and asked, "Are you lost? You be out here all by yourselves?" His head wasn't out of the front passenger's side window but still trying to stick his neck out the window enough to talk. The guy's long, greasy, brown hair was matted and tangled. There was a big scar across his nose area like he had been in an accident a few years ago. I noticed there were three of them in the car. The talker was telling the driver something.

I quickly said, "No, we just live over here in Jungle Park, and we're just walking into Palm Bay to get us a treat today."

"This back road is not a safe place for an old woman and a young boy to be walking, if you know what I mean," the fellow said, as he climbed out of the car, with a smaller boy getting out of the back on the other side, both coming toward us. The car drove off and the two continued to come toward us aggressively.

"Whoa…back up, kids," Granny said, as they approached. The boys looked about 18 or 20, not much bigger than me but close to adults because of the un-kempt beards. The biggest had long, stringy, light-brown hair, with pockmarks all over his face, with a sparse beard. The shorter, dark-haired guy was the talker or mouthier of the two.

"No, you better back up, old lady. We want some money, or we'll have that gold ring you're wearing, old lady," the bigger one said.

"Sorry, boys, that's not gold but silver and was made by my first husband out of a silver coin for our wedding because money was so scarce then. I don't think I can allow you to have that now. I do have some good chewing tobacco you can have some of." Granny spit a stream of tobacco juice right in the face of the biggest guy. He cried out, "What the hell is this?!" He grabbed his face and eyes.

Granny then hit the other boy square in the mouth with her cane, and blood flew. She turned back to the first one as he was clearing his eyes and struck him in the side of the head with her Shillelagh, that's what she used it like. She stood a head shorter than the biggest guy, as he kept ducking and weaving, trying to clear the tobacco juice from his eyes, nose and mouth and miss her flying brutal cane.

I grabbed the shorter one as he started toward Granny, and pulled him to the ground in a chokehold around his neck with my right arm. He kept trying to swing and punch, but I could feel him getting weaker the harder I squeezed. Granny went back over and kicked the big guy again as he tried to get up. He started yelling and yelping for help, looking for his ride.

Then Granny said, "No help here, buddy, it looks like your friend's left you to do the dirty work, and it's a little dirtier than you figured. Need any help over there, Johnny?"

She kicked the big boy's backside again as he crawled away up the road where his friend had gone in the car. She turned and struck the boy I had in a chokehold in the face with the cane, and blood spurted out of his nose and mouth, then he started yelling for help from his friend.

"Come on, Johnny, let him go; he's turning purple. There's not even a good fight in these two snotty-nosed young punks."

Granny and I left the two licking their wounds, going down the road looking for their friend. I didn't recognize any of them, but I kept looking over my shoulder. I'll sure watch out for their car from now on, thinking they might be part of a gang or something like that.

"We better hurry, Granny, I'm not sure when they close but that interruption took our ice cream time."

"Well, Johnny, it's like my Poppy used to say, I'm slow as cold molasses in the winter. After I was laid up with this broken hip for over a month after that wild horse threw me trying to break him, I never regained my speed like I once had. You might say, reckon he broke me instead of me breaking him." She laughed and spit the tobacco what seemed like a yard.

"Granny, where did you learn to fight like that? You could have handled them even without me. That cane of yours reminded me of a story I read of an old Irishman who was jumped by two thugs and he did what you did with what's called a Shillelagh old people used to walk with in Ireland, like a cane. Later, they used them as clubs, and now I can see how and why!" Then I laughed.

"I came up in a time where almost everything was a struggle. You had to learn to protect yourself, and your family, the best you could. I fortunately had older brothers who taught me and my sister Sarah how to defend ourselves," Grandma Rosie said, with sadness in her tone of voice.

"Granny, I can't get over how you can use that cane without hesitation."

"Johnny, it was either we get robbed or me use this cane on the side of their big head. I didn't really think, just reacted, much like I was trained to do shooting by a man a long time ago by the name of Jake. He taught me how to handle a six-shooter and a rifle during those days."

She simply said, "Let me tell you a story about when Tom and I went out West during the Yukon Gold Rush days." That's when she first told me about her travels out West, how she and Tom had struggled, fought and lived through those days. I had heard her tell Mom a few stories when I was smaller, but at that time I thought she would be around forever, never thinking that I should remember what she said.

We walked to the Ice Cream Shop, sat at a little round table, and ate our tasty treat as we talked about her adventures, many of which were way before my mother or I were even born. It was great to me, like listening to a history book being read to you, except you knew the characters.

That's when I started really listening to Grandma Rosie's stories and thinking about writing them into a book someday. I kept a journal for years, but it was lost during one of my many moves to different graduate schools. I came back home to see my parents in Henderson, Maryland. Uncle Rink, Aunt Elsie and family, Carol Ann, Diana and Timmy, had moved to Henderson to a little farm on the Maryland–Delaware state line called Mud Mill.

Granny told me many a story about Uncle Rink and Nora when they were young while I was with her down by the old Mud Mill Pond where we, the youngsters, would all go swimming in the summer and ice skating in the winter.

Granny lived there while I finished high school and the University of Maryland. She was really pleased when I became a high school teacher in the Maryland school system. At that time, Grandma Rosie was in her 90s. I again asked if she would mind sitting one day or evening to talk about her life.

Sgt William Howard Smith

***For those readers who do not know, I was adopted in a strange way. That was part of the reason for writing the book, *One Wild and Precious Life,* 2018 <u>Amazon.com.</u> This book tells the story, a select book by GoodReads.com.

Chapter 19

Your kids will remember the adventures you went on, not the stuff you bought them. Kids outgrow stuff, they never outgrow adventure.

Rosie 1950

Grandma Rosie Endures the Modern Era

I can remember, during high school, Grandma Rosie talking about the Nixon-Kennedy televised presidential debates during the early 1960s. She remembered presidents going around the country by train and speaking from the caboose area as their stump. "I'm a real Kennedy backer because he's handsome, smart and the true presidential type," she would say, while watching the news flashes on TV.

I never knew if she was a democrat or republican because she would never say. Only that, "I can remember when women didn't have the right to vote; now you can't keep us from the voting booth. I fought for our right to vote for many years. Now I will always vote, even though the candidates aren't what I think they should be."

She had a real difficult time with segregation, and the time I wanted to go to Washington, D.C. and march with the Freedom Riders when I was a senior in high school.

205

She felt there was no reason why there should have ever been segregation in the first place.

"That fight has already been fought and won; the black folks shouldn't have to march, demonstrate and fight for what they already have. Everyone was to be free and live free but somehow that never came about like it was supposed to happen. I know our family never had any problem with living beside or being friends with any color, no matter where they were from. As long as they treat me as I treated them, that was what I went by," Grandma said at that time.

"You know, Johnny, in Mohegan, Hemphill, Roderfield, and Welch, all the towns around there, all races and ethnic backgrounds lived together, and worked together without any trouble. The trouble started when outsiders came in from Chicago, Michigan, and New York, different areas telling different stories about whites, blacks, Jews or Catholics to stir up animosity. I never could understand why they did that."

One day I came home from football practice late and Mom had left dinner on the stove for me. Granny came in where I was and helped me get dinner warmed up. We were at the kitchen table, and Grandma said, "Johnny, explain something to me, you're smart, getting ready for college: why are they (the government) sending John Glenn up into space and risking his life when they have already proved even a monkey can do what's needed up there? We have much more important things to accomplish right now. The Cuban missile problem, there's still a problem trying to get people of different races to get along, poor Marilyn Monroe was found dead, and she had that handsome Kennedy in the palm of her hand."

"Grandma, you're watching too much TV. I can't keep up with all of the news. I didn't even know about Marilyn. Grandma, how old are you now?"

"Let's put it this way, I'm nearly ninety-five now; even I can't believe it. All of my old friends and most of my new friends I've met here in Henderson are dead. I can't believe all that I've seen and done. I used to ride wild horses, shoot, fight desperados, and now I'm watching them put a man on the moon," she said.

"Grandma, didn't you tell me to just take one day at a time, and to do the very best you can each day? Well, that's about all I can manage. I have a lot of schoolwork, my work at Thompson's Market, football practice, and several girlfriends that I have to keep happy. I'll tell you what, I'll be a graduate soon and we'll have a big party then, just you, me and all your friends."

"That sounds good. You know, it gets a little lonely here with everybody gone all day except me. I was thinking about taking a little trip but, after I thought about it, there's nowhere to go right now, except over yonder to Dover once in a while. I'm so proud of you. I want to hang around until you graduate from high school then see where you end up in college."

"Grandma, that will be next year if all goes according to plan. I'm trying to narrow it down but as you know there's very little financial resources coming from home. That means I need as much as I can in scholarship money. I'm writing to about five universities to see what help I can scrape up. Even Duck's dad, Mr. Thompson and Mr. Logan are searching for me. I think I'll be fine. You know me, I don't mind working my way through if I have to."

"You know I would give you a scholarship if I had the means, but all I get is a little check now each month. Tho, I hear they are fixin' to increase our checks any time now."

"Don't worry, Grandma, everything will be fine. I'm not worried."

Grandma Rosie came to my graduation at the University of Maryland in 1969 and watched me walk across the stage. However, she didn't come to the graduation from Palmer College in Davenport, Iowa, in 1976. She was not feeling strong at that time in her late 90s, so I asked her not to bother getting on a plane to make the trip with Mom and Dad.

In 1977, I was in practice in Delmar, Delaware. Grandma was still in good shape, sharp as a tack mentally the last time we talked that month. She was happy, and bright as could be. There was no sign whatsoever of senescence. The only thing I was concerned with was her weight, she was down to one hundred and two pounds. I had remembered in Florida, she was in her late 70s, and bragged about how she weighed more than Mom at 125. She never was very tall, but her hair was still long, dark, and very thick; it had only started to turn gray a few years earlier. When you looked at her, you could tell then there was some Indian genetics there, somewhere.

She kept talking about the wild music of this generation, especially the Beatles. Why couldn't they still play music you could listen to? Although by then she was beginning to like Elvis, because "He was a handsome young man, even if he shakes that thing too much, I would still let him put his shoes under my bed anytime," she would say.

I came in one evening when I was still living at home. She couldn't wait to tell me about the news she heard that day. As we talked, there was a wistful sound to her voice that I used to recognize when she told me stories about her life.

"Johnny, did you know that Winston Churchill died? He was a great leader. Your Aunt Elsie really thought the world of him, and what he did for the British people was wonderful, especially during and after WWII. Reckon he could get some type of medal or award for his leadership."

After I left for college, Grandma spent a great deal of time between Mom's and Uncle Rink and Aunt Elsie's, because Rink retired from International Latex where he worked as a guard, a perfect position for a former Army MP. He and Elsie took Grandma on trips to West Virginia, Virginia, and Kentucky to see relatives fairly often, especially Leona's and Hillard's children and grandchildren.

They even took Grandma up to the mountain where Tom Smith is buried to clean the site and show her his grave marker.

"It has been many years since I was here," she admitted.

Granny and I talked every week or two once I moved to the Eastern shore. She continued to socialize with friends there in Henderson, by having coffee each morning at Mom's house, or at one of the regular group's place. They loved to sit in the morning with their coffee and spread their view of a subject on the table, you might say. They were all in their 80s and 90s, several democrats, several republicans, an agnostic, an atheist; as you can imagine, they would have lively debates almost two or three times each week. She would have to tell me the ridiculous point of view of Omer, Carlton, Grover, Nellie, or one of the others.

The last time I saw her was at a little birthday party we threw her Saturday, April 8, at Mom's house, because that

Headstone of Tom Smith
Welch, West Virginia

was when and where most everyone could attend. There were about twenty people, mostly her family and close friends. We had a party for her at ninety-five because she said, "It was as old as I remembered anyone in the family ever living to be. It's a lot of work living, you know, past your working age."

On April 10, 1978, just a few days before I was to go up to Henderson for my brother Doug's birthday on April 12, Mom called about seven and said, "Johnny, I think you better come up today; your grandmother isn't doing well and I'm not sure how long she will be here. She started this morning around six with her not being able to drink or eat anything and gotten worse from there. We thought it was from her eating so much birthday cake Saturday. I'll tell you the whole story when you get here."

I left Delmar right away and it took me about an hour to get there. When I arrived, Mom asked me to sit down, she had something to tell me. I could tell by the look on her face it was something serious because her eyes were all red like she had been crying.

"Your grandmother, Rosie, is gone; she died this morning after you left to come up here. We had to send her by ambulance to Kent General Hospital in Dover. She was there about an hour before she passed. She died of 'essentially old age,' Dr. Jarrell said. 'There was nothing else we could find; she just went to sleep.'"

A service was held in Greensboro, a small town south of Henderson, Maryland, where there is a family plot.

I have compiled the facts as close as I can remember about Grandma Rosie's life. I have put an emphasis on the Yukon Gold Rush days, because to me those days were her most outstanding, when she was young, wild and free. Even Tom, big, handsome and smart, couldn't contain her positive energy when there was something she wanted to do.

After reading this narrative, email me and let me know just how you feel about this chronicle. There are a few more stories she told my mother and me that are certainly worth telling again, if there's enough time and interest.

Headstone of Rosie Runyon Smith Pendergrass –
Greensboro, MD

About the Author

John L. Stump was born in 1946 in Welch, West Virginia, and was educated at the University of Maryland. He completed his doctoral training at Palmer College of Chiropractic in Davenport, Iowa, and Post-doctoral (PhD) at Shannix College in China, and a third doctoral degree (EdD) in Sports Medicine at the United States Sports Academy. After returning from the 1988 Olympics, where he was a team doctor, he settled down on the Gulf Coast in Fairhope, Alabama.

Dr. Stump spent forty-five years as a chiropractic physician specializing in acupuncture and nutrition and wrote several professional books, including *Somatovisceral Aspects of Chiropractic; Energy Medicine: East and West; Applied Kinesiology Essentials: The Missing Link;* and *A Stroke of Midnight. The Beacon* referred to him as "the poet laureate of natural medicine," and over the years he received many recognitions and awards in the United States, as well as from Japan, India, China and Korea, where he taught and studied. One

213

of his favorite authors was Oliver Sacks.

Dr. Stump's early life memoir, *One Wild and Precious Life.* His harrowing ordeal of a near fatal stroke can be read in the book, *A Stroke of Midnight,* and the pandemic release in 2020 of *Undeterred* tells of his professional life and travels to the 1988 Olympic games as a physician. His latest work in 2021 will be *Rambling Rosie Runyon* based on the life of his grandmother in 1890's. He is retired now from active practice and devotes his time to his family, grandchildren, writing, lectures and travel.

Made in the USA
Columbia, SC
28 July 2021